NEVER HAVE I EVER

A MEMOIR

DIARY OF A ONCE SURLY,
EX-JADED, HIGH-MAINTENANCE WRECK
ON AN EXTRAVAGANT MISSION TO
ACCOMPLISH ABSOLUTE FIERCENESS
OR SOMETHING LIKE THAT

ALLISTER DEAN

—FOR THOSE WHO WANT MORE
IN LIFE, TAKE A DEEP YOGA INHALE
AND JUST FUCKING DO IT!

*"Thirty was so strange for me.
I've really had to come to terms with the fact
that I am now a walking and talking adult."*
—C. S. Lewis

• •

"He who leaves a trail of glitter is never forgotten."
—Unknown

• •

"Fill your cracks with gold!"
—Lucy

NEVER
HAVE
I EVER

A MEMIOR

Prologue

The Glitter List

"Never have I ever...travelled outside the country," Ezra said, looking around at the other players.

Jeez! Say something I can use!

A few people in the circle of nine put down one finger while the rest waited, trying to keep their tired hands raised, including mine. If you haven't figured it out by now, yes, us grownups are playing the high school drinking game *Never Have I Ever*—but with wine. Bruce had suggested the idea to us after dinner.[1]

"Never have I ever...been impulsive," Colton said next.

"What do you mean by impulsive?" I asked.

"Like, doing something without giving it a second

---

[1] More like bullied everyone into playing.

thought."

I, yet again, didn't put down any fingers.[2] Still at five fingers, people! Impulsive...what a dumb thing to ask. Anything I ever did always constituted an overthinking session of what might happen if I acted upon the action. More times than not, I ended up not following through.

"Never have I ever...had sex in public," Olivia proudly said.

Becoming irritated that none of my fingers budged, I took a sip of my red wine.

"Allister! Have you really?" Olivia asked, perking up.

"Um, No. I was thirsty."

Who wants to have an indecent exposure charge under their belt for the rest of their life? Let's also not forget having to register as a sex offender.

"Never have I ever..."

I interrupted him. "Sorry to stop you there, James, but this guy needs to head home. It's getting a wee bit late and my dogs are probably doing the potty dance," I said, finishing off the rest of my wine.

Olivia—a tall, brunette bombshell who should have ventured into modeling instead of hosting wonderful dinner parties—got up from her seat and walked me to the front door after saying my goodbyes to everybody.

I jovially grabbed her hands in mine and said, "Thank you, Olivia, for having me. The dinner was fabulous, as al-

---

[2] So, for those who have never played its simple. You're in a circle holding up five fingers. The object of the game is to say things you've never done knowing full well that other people in the circle have, one finger goes down. You keep going round until no one has any fingers up. Phew! Are we good?

ways."

"You're very welcome. You okay to drive home?" she asked, concerned.

"Of course. I didn't have very much wine tonight."

"You're always welcome to crash here."

"Much as I want to have a slumber party, I'm a responsible doggy daddy." I smiled and hugged her goodbye.

While driving through residential areas and dodging police-infested check points, I felt hung up on the dumb game Bruce made us play. Why did it bother me so much? Was it the fact that most of the people at the party had done more in their twenties than me? I've published two books; that's got to count for something!

Then, it hit me: I've become a boring extrovert.

Before my lovely stay at the hospital earlier this year—which I will never go back to—my fat ass had been spending large amounts of time in front of Netflix, sucking down boxed wine while stuffing my face with potato chips. I found more pleasure receiving postal mail than going out to the clubs.

Carrie Bradshaw mentioned that your twenties were to be marvelous and filled with vibrancy. I, on the other hand, miserably failed to enjoy mine. I wasted the years, really. And now, I'm on the verge of turning thirty.[3]

THIRTY!

No way will I leave my twenties or enter my thirties

---

[3] The official age of gay death.

with nothing to show! We've reached DEFCON 1, people. Time after time, I see people on Facebook create life events or make unforgettable memories not only for themselves, but with their close friends.

As I reflect on the game from earlier, I realize that in life, I always thought something through and ended up not doing following through if it seemed risky. I now realize that has got to change because I can no longer say no to opportunities.

Wait, so what exactly am I proposing here?

Making it home before eleven, I let my pooches out in the back yard and grab a pen and paper so I can write down all the things I've always wanted to accomplish.

---

1. LEARN TO SKI
2. UNDIE RUN
3. GROW A BEARD
4. HAVE A PEN PAL
5. VOTE
6. FOLSOM STREET FAIR
7. LEARN FRENCH
8. SHOOT A GUN
9. WALK IN HIGH-HEELS[4]
10. STEAL A STREET SIGN
11. MEET THE MAYOR
12. STRIPPER BAR
13. KISS A STRAIGHT MAN

---

[4] Strangely, I've always wanted to do that.

14. CRASH A WEDDING
15. AUDITION FOR A PLAY
16. BE A GUEST ON A PODCAST
17. SKINNY DIP
18. GET PUBLISHED BY A WELL KNOWN PUBLICATION
19. TRY YOGA
20. RIDE A MECHANICAL BULL[5]
21. MAKE MY OWN CLOTHES
22. CAMPING
23. WALKING IN A MARCH
24. GO TO A NUDE BEACH
25. ARCHERY
26. NEW YEARS IN STYLE
27. MEET A CELEBRITY
28. TRY A NEW FOOD
29. HAVE A NEW YEAR'S EVE MIDNIGHT KISS
30. TAKE A TRAIN

An hour later, and two more glasses of wine, a list of thirty items presented itself to me. Yes, some of the items are lame, but it's my list and I'll do what I want! Thirty items over the a course of a year is doable, right? Until now, I was leading a very vanilla life I didn't sign up for.

Glitter list extravaganza, here I come!

---

[5] Make sure 911 is on speed dial.

365

Extravagant Gays on Social Media,

How the FUCK can you afford to travel and live extravagantly with your rooftop parties, boating excursions on the lakes, drinking champagne on the daily, and just doing whatever comes to mind when clearly you're an assistant of some sort or work in a call center from the selfies you post on Instagram or Snapchat? The headset gave it away darlin', along with the name of the company plastered on the wall behind you or the far-as-I-can-see cubicles landscaping your backdrop. Last time I checked, neither of those professions bring home the bacon.

And yet, somehow, you're doing it.

Did you make a deal with the devil to achieve this lifestyle?[6]

If so, all I can say is this...SHIT! I've signed my life away multiple times on the dotted line and STILL haven't received any form of luxury payment. I must have gotten one of those offers that turned into a scam, like the kind where you can enjoy a three-day weekend in Aspen, CO—all expenses paid—but you have to attend their timeshare conference. At first, the timeshare people make you believe it's only going to take an hour or so, but surprise! The confer-

---

[6] Or, are you simply loaning your body out just for the sake of hot-tubbing on a Tuesday?

ence is an everyday event that steals precious time from mini-vacay you've been dying to enjoy.

The closest I've ever been to living the extravagant life was on Cinco de Mayo over a year ago. Though the holiday is socially Americanized, I enjoyed it by submerging myself in a lime green baby pool I set up in my backyard while sipping down bottomless margaritas and wearing an oversized sombrero. It probably wasn't my best idea, especially when my gated-community neighbors happened to walk by. Those with children who nosily peered through the fence witnessed the beginnings of my intoxicated holiday as I attempted to sing along to music but ended up singing much louder than the speaker playing the music.

There's Instagram evidence deep in its catacombs of this solo performance, but I hope nobody will take the time to unearth the tragedy that I considered to be extravagant.

But the question still remains...

How can you afford to travel, explore, and party with such a low-paying job?

Always,

Allister

July 8, 2018

Dear August,

Pretty fucking stoked about becoming pen pals, just saying!

Not exactly sure where to start as I've never had a pen pal before. Might as well just dive in and get the ball rolling, haha.

Can't believe this month is almost over. It seems like yesterday that I was ringing in the New year. I guess when you're a busy bee, there is not enough time in the day. I feel maybe some introductions are in order. My name is Allister Dean, age twenty-nine, and I'm a writer. I used to be a photographer, but I felt words were more my calling. Don't get me wrong, I loved photography and still practice it from time to time, but nowadays everybody thinks they're a photographer. So, the feeling of uniqueness has slowly dwindled.

I have two younger brothers that I have not seen or spoken to in seven years, by choice. My mother and father are divorced, but recently my mother remarried to a wonderful gentleman not too long ago in Ireland. Just like my brothers, I don't talk to my father as he's a very toxic person—just like the cigarettes he consumes.

I'm currently single and loving every minute of it. The only two men that occupy my time are Mercury and Mars. They are the two Chihuahuas I rescued about two years ago when they were eight months old. Mercury is a rambunctious, tan pooch who sometimes embodies an old man. He sits at the corner of the couch, closest to the window where the sidewalk can be seen, and barks as people walk past. I swear Mercury is truly saying, "get off my lawn." Mars is the complete opposite. He's a timid, black and white puppy who has relearned to trust people again. Right off the bat, I could tell he was abused. When anyone tried to pet him, he urinated. Mars had problems, too. He constantly hid his food in a blanket. Now, they're not the same dogs I brought home— they're much happier.

Recently, a good friend of mine took me to the movies and dinner at my favorite restaurant called *Liberty*[7]. It's locally owned and they produce their own wine. Can't beat that!

Always,

Allister

To: *Allister_at_home*

---

[7] My very first hetero date and I loved it!

From: *August_at_home*
Subject: RE: *Letter One — Introductions*

July 13, 2018

Hi Allister,

Good to hear from you and nice to meet you! I'm James, thirty-nine, and I'm an Executive Producer at a TV station in east Texas. TV news tends to move me around every few years. Previously, I was the News Director at K*** in your hometown. I absolutely love what I do. At times, especially the older I get, it feels like "kid stuff" and news sometimes seems less relevant than it once was. All things considered, I love getting to tell other people's stories and each story brings something new and different.

I feel blessed enough to know what I really loved doing from an early age. I was a theater major for one semester in college. I also was in plays and musicals during high school. However, I quickly (and wisely) realized I wasn't cut out for acting.

If I had to do it over again, perhaps writing plays or screen plays would have been more up my alley, but coulda, woulda, shoulda... When I was a kid, I used to take my tape recorders and link them together so I could mix in between two tapes and microphone. I would pretend to be on the radio. Later on, I realized I liked English. So, everything kind of came together to make broadcast journalism a very good fit for me.

After college (University of Central Oklahoma), I made working stops in several cities, Fort Smith, AR., Oklahoma City (my hometown), Tampa, FL., New York City, Tulsa, OK., Abilene, TX., Reno, NV., and now Tyler, TX. New York City was my dream market as I loved the years spent there.

When I was ready to settle down, I accepted a bigger challenge than reporting and producing and went into new management. I discovered a love for leading and shaping news coverage. Handling the interesting and sometimes defective personalities that news tends to draw (myself included) can be challenging, but that doesn't bother me in the least.

I currently don't have pets, but I love cats and dogs. For a while, I had a streak of bad pet luck that makes me wonder if I am the grim reaper of pets. Basically, about a year ago I had to put my cat down. He still had a decent quality of life, but he was FIV+ (cat aids) and started peeing everywhere. The vets unsuccessfully treated him for urinary tract infections. He couldn't be an outdoor cat because he'd flip out. The vet said euthanasia was a good option, so that was that. Fast forward a year—or about two weeks ago—when I adopted a rescue dog. She was perfect, house trained, calm, friendly, but unusually lethargic.

Suspecting something was wrong, I took her to the vet the

day after adopting her, and they told me she had a very serious condition: her body no longer produced red blood cells, and the ones she had were being attacked by her immune system.

At my vet's advice, I took her back to the SPCA. They got a second opinion from a different vet who diagnosed her with the same condition. Understandably, she was put to sleep. I'm going to take it all as a sign from the cosmos that I'm not meant to have animals, at least not right now.

I'm currently dating someone here in Texas. It's fun, but also not really going great. He's younger than me, cute, and fun to be with. He also wants sex all the time. What's the problem, right? Well, he's polyamorous, which I really don't judge. Don't get me wrong; when I was in my early twenties, I liked to slut around a lot, hey, it was fun.

However, now that I'm thirty-nine, I really want someone who has the potential of becoming a long-term partner.[8] He is not that partner. We both have biting, sarcastic senses of humor that complement one another, but I just can't do FWB's anymore.

Outside of my struggling love life, I have a younger brother who is eight years my junior. He and his wife have three kids. I also stay in touch with my mother and stepdad, but I am estranged from my biological father. I haven't spoken

---

[8] Preaching to the choir!

with him for the past six months.

I miss your hometown at times. I am not a health nut, but I loved the kale salad at Campo in the downtown area. Good stuff.

August

---

4. HAVE A PEN PAL

1

Beardiful

FYI:

I wrote my glitter list back in December of 2017 before being stricken with pneumonia five months later—it's now June 2017. Getting sick threw a huge monkey wrench in my plans for achieving certain items on the glitter list. Little did I know I would accomplish one of the items on my list while in the suffering from pneumonia: Grow a beard.

It's always been a huge challenge to grow a beard because I could never get past the itchy stage. As soon as my face started itching, it was hello shaver and bye-bye week-old facial hair. I had accepted the fact that I was not worthy to wield a mighty beard.

To my surprise, all it took was an unplanned hospital stay—for two weeks—where razors and any other forms of shaving materials were restricted.

Total nightmare, if you ask me.

• • • • •

DAY ONE:
2:00 PM

"You have bilateral pneumonia, which means both of your lungs are filled with fluid. We have to admit you. A nurse is on her way with a wheelchair to take you to a room we've prepped for you," the doctor said as a male nurse held up my x-ray.

"The last time I had this, I was ten," I replied in shock.

"Since you've had it before, you're more susceptible to getting it again."

"Basically, what you're telling me is that it felt like a reunion was necessary." I said, raising my voice.

The doctor didn't say a word as he walked out of my temporary room in the ER.

"What a dick," I said, loud enough for the other nurses to hear me.

• • • • •

DAY TWO:
3:30 AM

Someone knocked at the door and woke me.

"Good morning, I'm hear to take some of your blood," a young woman in a white lab coat announced.

"Do you know what time it is?" I quietly asked.

"I do apologize, but it'll take two seconds."

"Can you tell me what this is for?"

There is no way I'm allowing a needle to enter my body if it's not necessary.[9] Having a mother in the medical field taught me to ask exactly whats being done, otherwise, hospitals tend to take advantage of their patients and rack up bills to make a quick buck.

"I'm not exactly sure. I get the orders from your doctors and send them off to get tested," the nurse stated.

"Each one of those tubes has a colored top that indicates what you're testing for. So, you should know. Before you stick that needle in my arm, please find out what it's for and don't come back in until you do. If you don't mind, I would like to go back to sleep," I confidently said.

The phlebotomist raised her eyebrows and looked at the clear, empty vials.

"Well?" I asked.

"Let me see what I can find out," she muttered. She turned, walked out of the room, and never came back.

• • • • •

DAY FIVE:
6:47 PM

---

[9] People are afraid of snakes, bears, water...needles are my phobia.

I was on the toilet when a nurse came rushing into my room like a badass from hell, kicking down the restroom door...

"Is everything okay?" she hollered.

Screaming, I closed my legs and told her to get the fuck out. Apparently, I set off the heart monitor or some important alarm, triggering who ever was watching to come check on me.[10]

• • • • •

DAY SEVEN:
8:15 AM

"Hello, how are you feeling?" the doctor asked.

"Is this a trick question or are you being serious?" I answered, my voice conveying my irritation.

Dr. Worthington—a tall, light blonde, medium build man—gave an unsure glare as his body language shifted from confidence to hesitance in a second. I don't think he expected someone so abrasive at eight in the morning.

"I've been here for a week now and you keep asking the same question since I've been admitted. Why do you come in here when you know that I still feel like shit? Unless you have new information about what kind of pneumonia I have, don't bother coming into my room!" I snapped.

"Well, I always want to make sure my patients are doing

---

[10] If my heart rate was elevated, it's through the roof now.

better than the day before. How's the rash?" Dr. Worthington asked.

"Gone, no thanks to you. By the way, I want a portion of you salary as it's clearly apparent I did your job by figuring out I was allergic to the medication you prescribed. Did you actually complete medical school or did you copy someones homework?"

Making himself at home by sitting on my bed, the blonde doctor smirked and looked at the tiny loveseat that contained my forest green man-bag.

"That's a nice bag," he said, admiring it.

"Thanks. It's a limited edition bag Apple designed. 175 bucks later, I owned one," I boasted. My curiosity was peaked. Straight men don't comment on bags like that, especially one owned by a gay man. Looking at his hand, I saw there was no ring. Doctors usually marry a trophy wife within a year or two of receiving their degree. Otherwise, the whole medical ensemble is incomplete.

Oh...my...god, he's flirting with me.

It's the only thing that makes sense! He comes in everyday with no news, but instead makes small talk and sits usually close to me—too close at that—yes, this man is gay! My gaydar's Richter scale is through the roof!

"If there is nothing else to discuss, there's the door. I've got some catching up to do with the Kardashians," I said, turning on the T.V.

• • • • •

DAY NINE:

12:45 AM

"How long have you been like this?" the respiratory therapist asked.

"For twenty minutes. I called for a nurse but no one came," I said, stuttering.

She wasn't happy...she was pissed. The nurse who was assigned to me that day neglected my call when I knew something was wrong. I was shivering so severely that my bed was squeaking. The second therapist, who accompanied the first respiratory therapist, told me to breath deeply through my nose and exhale out my mouth.

"I need you to do that for five minutes," he said.

The first therapist turned up the oxygen to the maximum level. Both of them started breathing along with me until I normalized. At that time, the neglectful nurse who I called for strolled into my room like she could care less.

"Is everything okay?" she asked.

I gave her a death stare.

"You! Where the hell have you been? Allister was at an oxygen level of fifty percent!" the first respiratory therapist aggressively conveyed.

"Bet you were."

I was stunned, but I didn't let the first-hand *General Hospital* drama affect me. It seemed as though my assigned nurse had already earned herself a bad reputation. This was so much better than watching the Kardashians. After all, one can only take so much monotoned stupidity in a few hours.

I spoke up with a sickeningly sweet voice. "How about this? Why don't we assign someone else to me so this doesn't happen again? Otherwise, this neglectful nurse is going to end up killing me and nobody wants that."

"That's a good idea, I'll go ahead speak with the head nurse," the respiratory therapist said with a knowing smile.

LATER THAT DAY...

10:05 PM

"I'm going to take some blood," a male nurse said as fifteen medical personal entered my room. My heart rate became extremely elevated. This was probably to fix what the neglectful nurse did—or didn't—do for me earlier. The man who wanted to draw my blood looked familiar, but I couldn't place him.

"You're going to take blood from my knuckle?" I quizzically asked.

"Yeah," he said with a smile.

"Don't think that's going to work."

"I've done this a million times," he confidently said.

Irritation bubbled up inside me as the needle poked around and started to hurt my finger. No blood came forth.

"Think you're done," I told him.

"I almost got it," he replied.

"You have ten seconds to cease or I'm going to deck you," I firmly said.

His eyes locked with mine. Then it hit me—I knew where I'd seen him before.

"Now, since you don't like to listen, you can march your ass out of my room Grindr profile Masc4Med."

"I don't know what you're talking about," he said looking embarrassed.

"So, this isn't you?"

I pulled my phone out, went straight to his profile, tapped on his picture, and held it up for everyone to see.

"Says here you like to choke on big cock," I said.

A lovely shade of red flushed his cheeks.

"All right, I think you need to rest," another nurse said, breaking the tension.

She handed me a white pill—made sure I took it—and told everybody to leave the room.

"Bye, Masc4Med," I loudly said.

• • • • •

DAY TWELVE:
8:45 AM

"I want to keep you one more day just to be on the safe side," Dr. Worthington said.

"That's not going to happen. I can't stay here another day because I'm gonna go crazy," I told him, stuffing my mouth full of pancakes.

"Let's make you deal. When you go on your walk later today with the nurse and your oxygen level stays above ninety, I'll discharge you. But, if doesn't, another day you'll stay."

I didn't know doctors made deals like that. If he said no, I was going to walk out anyway. There was no reason for me to stay if I was feeling better, especially when nobody here was doing their job correctly.

"Deal," I said.

When the doctor left my room and I was alone, I jumped out of bed and paced around the room, desperate to maintain my oxygen level. However, it kept falling under 90%. How the hell was I going to get out of here? Remembering what the respiratory therapist had me do the other day, I began to breathe in through my nose and out my mouth while walking circles in my room.

It worked.

A FEW HOURS LATER

Practice makes perfect as they say, and I managed to keep my O^2 in the nineties. After calling for the nurse, a young blonde guy waltzed into my room.

"What's up?" he asked.

"I'm ready to take my walk," I confidently said.

"Let me grab a mobile oximeter and we'll go."

Nodding, I removed the stationary one I was attached to and sat in the chair by the door and waited. Why was I so nervous? The last time I felt like this, it was behind the wheel of my parents car when I hoped to ace my driving test on the first try.[11]

"Are you ready?" the male nurse said, scaring the crap out of me.

"Ready as I'll ever be," I confidently said.

---

[11] Which I did!

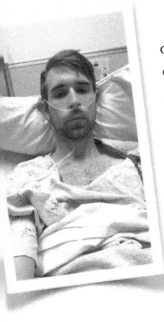

While the nurse connected the oximeter to my finger, I looked up and down the long hallway. My room was dead center. Why can't hospital hallways be short and sweet? Taking a deep breath, the nurse and I turned left down the hallway. Not thinking about anything else, I just kept saying to myself, *deep breathes in through my nose, then out my mouth.*

"Are you doing okay? the nurse asked.

"Shhhhhhhhhh," I silenced him.

He didn't take kindly to being told to shut up, but, he had to understand I couldn't have any distractions. One wrong move and I would be chained to my room again, left to deal deal with three-in-the-morning blood draws, useless doctors, and neglectful nurses. Thank God for the double chocolate brownies that came with lunches and dinners and kept me sane. Otherwise, I would have choked a bitch by now.

In no time flat we had finished walking the first half of the long hallway, and now we were coming to the end of the second half. This was my make it or break it moment. But, I was determined to get out of this hell hole they called a hospital. As we headed back up the hallway and to my room, I paused to compose myself a little. Even if you're getting better, breathing still takes a lot out of you.

Rising quickly, I watched the monitor like a hawk even though the nurse hadn't. I don't think he really cared, which was a total shame. Not once during our enchanted stroll had it dropped below the requisite 92% oxygen level, which told me I would go home very soon.

Back in my room, I began packing up all that belonged to me. I instructed the male nurse to have Dr. Worthington promptly discharge me. The nurse advised I wouldn't be able to leave until later that evening. Nodding my head at him, he excused himself to complete the task.

My mother arrived an hour after I called her. She had stopped by my apartment to grab fresh clothes for me to change in. I also requested my biggest pair of sunglasses with the darkest tinted lens. I wanted to leave a lasting impression on the staff by channeling my inner Miranda from *The Devil Wears Prada*.

Some of the other nurses I had made a connection with said their goodbyes and hugged me. At the elevators, I noticed the nurse who had a bad reputation—the one who neglected me several days ago. She turned and offered the fakest smile.

"I'm sad to see you go," she said.

"I'm not," I replied.

"Well, I wish you the best of luck."

I motioning for the discharge nurse who was wheeling me out to continue on because I had nothing else to say to the neglectful nurse.

Oh wait, I did...

"Don't kill anyone else while I'm gone!" I hollered at the top of my lungs, waving goodbye.

3. ~~GROW A BEARD~~

To: Eve_ *at_ home, Kitty_ at_ home,*
From: *Allister_ at_ home*
Subject: *Karma's a Bitch*

July 02, 2018

Girls,

First things first, I'm feeling so much better! Sorry for not reaching out sooner to fill you both in on how I was doing. Recovering from pneumonia still takes a lot of one's energy. My new doctor, though, is a miracle worker who got me back on my feet and moving again within two weeks. If he's able to help his patients with a speedy recovery, he needs to work on turning water into wine...just saying. Now, I need to gain back the weight I lost in the hospital. Twenty pounds may not seem like a lot, but, it makes a drastic difference in appearance. All that hard work at the gym with my personal trainer kicking my ass six days a week went to shit.

But, I'm not writing to bitch about that.

Always,

Allister

2

The Devil Wears Rainbow Socks

"Why so late?" I asked Margaret, my PR agent.

I was excited because she had scheduled a book signing at a book store in my hometown about two months after I was released from the hospital—which really felt a prison. What she forgot to tell me was that I would be sharing a table with two other authors. If she had it her way, she would have had people show up in my bedroom so I could do a reading and signing.

"That's the slot they had available. I tried to get one earlier, but it was either this time or nothing at all," Margaret said in an unconvincing tone.[12]

---

[12] More like she didn't care.

Begrudgingly doing as I was told, a tall woman who re-sembled my old girl scout supervisor greeted me. Even her mannerisms were the same.

"Allister, right?" she asked, an uncertain tone in her voice.

"You got it," I said, removing my sunglasses.

"I'm Janet, and you're early, I'm still setting up."

"Sorry, I like to look around before anything gets start-ed. Would you like any help?" I asked.

"You're sweet, I'm actually just about done."

Janet filled me in on what to expect and who the other authors were: a fantasy writer and an author with a very in-teresting book about the homeless. She really didn't have the words to describe what her book was all about. As our forced conversation faded, she perked up and suggested I get myself set up.

A young boy around ten years old wandered over and asked if I was an author. Nodding my head, we made small talk.

"Do you like to read?" I asked.

"I do! Mainly chapter books. My mom does, too," he excitedly said.

"What's the last book you read?"

"I don't remember, it's at home."

"Do you want to be an author when you grow up?"

"No, I want to make computers," he said.

"That's really cool," I replied, trying to sound excited.

Speaking with this boy almost felt like I was interview-ing him for a job and I hoped that his mother would come and take him away. Don't get me wrong, I like kids, but there's only so much we can talk about.

Being a good sport, I sat in my chair and listened to what the boy had to say, even though he spoke with incomplete sentences. My focus shifted to the left side of kid's head. There were two extra-long, stray blonde hairs bouncing up and down. It became obvious to me that his house was a make-shift salon and his mama was hair stylist. All I wanted to do was help a brother out and decapitate those rebel hairs, but it wouldn't look very good if people saw me wielding a pair of scissors over this kid's head.

It took me second to realize that he had stopped talking and wanted a response from me.

"Oh, that's cool!" I said.

The little boy didn't buy it and he raised an eyebrow at me.

I didn't know what to say after that.

"You must be Allister," an older lady said. She wore big sunglasses and an uncombed, platinum wig.

"Yep, that's me," I said, standing.

The young boy walked away and turned to take one last look at me before disappearing in the back of the store. He didn't give off that *Children of the Corn* creepy vibe...at all.

"Hi, I'm Joy," the wigged woman exuberantly said while delicately shaking my hand. Joy resembled an unkempt Anna Wintour.[13] She wore an oversized black blazer, a black skirt, black tights, rainbow socks which had decent sized holes, and black crocs to finish off the look.[14] Joy's personal-

---

[13] Fashion Icon and the closest I'll ever get to meeting her. That's all.

[14] There are possibilities here; either she came from a gay funeral or was the gay angel of death to come take me away.

ity was bubbly, like a just freshly opened champagne bottle. It seemed like nothing could bring her down.

"I'm Stanley," a voice behind her announced.

A thirty-something-year-old man shook my hand and presented himself as the third author for the event. I couldn't take him seriously. He wore a silk button up shirt that had a printed anime character on it. Janet came over and greeted the other authors, then explained what her expectations were for the event.

• • • • •

Stanley had already published three books—a trilogy—while Joy only had one book she published years ago. It wasn't a novel of any sort. Rather, it was a fifteen page—not including the front and back covers—picture book of homeless people with blurbs here and there she was selling for twenty-two dollars.

"I think you should move to the Castro, Allister. You'll do so well there,"[15] Joy said, out of the blue.

"You think? I've visited the Castro many times when Gay Pride came around. It's vibrant," I said with a chuckle.

"I love it there! The gays are simply amazing," she replied.

The fantasy writer between us didn't say a word. Instead, he enjoyed playing with the Sharpies he carried in a tiny metal box until a loud group of distracted woman slammed into our table. The sudden table jolt scared the

---

[15] It's because I'm gay, isn't it?

shit out of him and knocked the metal box and his prized Sharpies out of his hand. They clattered to the floor, frustrating him.

The ladies ogled at our books. One grabbed mine and read the synopsis.

"Are these books about you?" she asked.

"Indeed. Both books are memoirs," I said with a smile.

"Interesting."

"If you like *Sex and the City* and *Bridget Jones's Diary*, you'll love it," I said.

"Sold! Make it out to Cindy."

Out of the four women, two of them bought a signed copy, leaving the other authors with no sales. In your face, fantasy writer!

• • • • •

A nervous woman approached the table. She looked as if she had something on her mind but didn't know how to say it. Joy picked up on that vibe, and unwittingly placed the spotlight on the poor woman.

"Do you have something you want to say or are you going to keep it bottled up?" Joy asked.

Jesus, have a little tact, Joy.

"Oh...um...how did you all get your start?" she asked.

"Honey, it's our calling," Joy said, placing a hand on her cheek.

I spoke up. "I think what she means is that we started with an idea...an idea we wanted to share with others. After that, it's about finding the right publisher who shares the same vision."

"Let Mama help you with that. After all, I've been in the business for thirty-five years. Take my business card," Joy said, pursing her dried lipstick lips.

Mama needed to make up her mind. Either help this woman or keep telling her that it takes a special kind of person to be in this business. Feeling bad, I advised her to finish her book first, but casually seek out an editor, copy editor, and publisher. The woman nodded gratefully for the new-found info. I could tell she didn't want to come off as rude for not listening to Joy anymore, and I couldn't blame her. Joy was no help what-so-ever.

• • • • •

With only fifteen minutes left in our time slot, I was still in the lead for the most books sales.[16] I could tell Joy had become irritated because her book wasn't selling. I must admit, she played cool really well. I wasn't sure what was going on with Stanley. Having only sold one book himself, he remained quiet.

"It's time for Mama to hit the wine," Joy said as she stroked her messy wig.

"I would have to agree with Joy," I added.

Janet appeared at the table and handed each of us an envelope with our cuts in it, which was something new. I asked her why we were receiving the money up front.

"Our bookstore has done it like that forever," she said

---

[16] Yes, I was secretly competing even though we were not in the same genre.

with a shrug.

It didn't answer my question, but I wasn't going to argue.

Joy grabbed my hands and suggested that we should hangout if ever found myself in San Francisco. Stanley didn't stick around. Instead, he quickly waved goodbye to everyone, walked out the front door, and drove away in his red minivan. That guy was a walking cliché, I swear!

Later, I called my PR agent and let her know the event went well. I also instructed her not to book anymore signings with other authors. After sharing a table for a couple of hours, I realized Daddy is better off solo.

3

Quick Getaway

— SAN JOSE —

"Now boarding flight 2350 from Reno to San Jose," a deeply-voiced woman said over the intercom.

That was my flight, and I'm not going to lie, I was a little scared. This would be the first time I've taken a plane by myself. In the past, there always had been someone with me—my parents when I was twelve on a trip to Seattle, and later an ex who decided that after two months of dating, a surprise Valentine's Day trip to San Diego was acceptable.[17] A sweet gesture at best, but the only event that was memo-

---

[17] I got his a $60 watch.

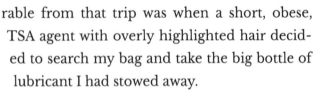

rable from that trip was when a short, obese, TSA agent with overly highlighted hair decided to search my bag and take the big bottle of lubricant I had stowed away.

"I'm going to have to confiscate this," she loudly announced.

Highly embarrassed, I saw the people behind me in line look over and notice what she held in her hand.[18]

"Why?" I asked.

"It's too big," she said.

And then, my unfiltered wittiness made surfaced and took over. "Is that the first time you've said that?"

Completely surprised I didn't end up in airport jail, I've since learned to smile, nod, keep my mouth shut, and not pack anything that large again. Being dragged out of an airport isn't on my Glitter List, especially after what happened to that man on the United plane.

TSA already has me filled with unwanted anxiety, so I didn't pack a toothbrush or tooth paste on this trip. I figured I would pick that up in San Jose.

---

[18] Yes, I did pack lubricant because my boyfriend at the time and I we're going to have mad sex while in Cali.

One by one, each passenger scanned in their ticket while an energetic woman greeted us. We all headed down the metal jetway to a very small, personal jet-sized Alaska plane that waited on the tarmac. Most of the passengers where checking their bags with a man who stood next to a metal cart at the bottom of the boarding stairs.

NOPE!

No need to get my weekender bag lost somehow, and knowing my streak of luck, it would happen to me. No doubt about it. Rushing past him and clutching my bag close to me, I quickly boarded the plane.

Another Alaska employee greeted me: "Welcome, glad to have you on board with us this evening," she said.

I didn't even acknowledge her as I quickly headed to my assigned seat, 13A. The interior of the plane was smaller than I expected. There were only seventeen rows, each with two seats on each side. It felt like a sardine container. Even the overhead bins were smaller and could only fit backpacks and purses. Is this how they get you to check your bags and make you pay extra? Smart move Alaska, smart move.

A very well-groomed man in his mid-thirties, dressed in a slimming blue suit with a red tie, waited for me in the aisle seat, 13B. His eyes were a deep blue, the kind that can see right into your soul.

"Hi, I do apologize for making you get up...but...that is my seat," I politely said.

"Which would you prefer, the window or aisle seat?" he kindly asked.

Surprised that he offered, I still choose my assigned window seat. Mr. Red Tie stood and side-stepped into the aisle, allowing me to pass by him. Like I said, we were packed like sardines. I placed my bag under the seat in front of me, where it fit snuggly. Then, I buckled myself into my seat and waited for take off. Mr. Red Tie did the same.

In a matter of minutes, the plane filled up and the flight attendants strolled down the aisle, checking the overhead bin doors to make sure they were tightly closed. One of them—a cake-faced attendant—asked a woman to put her purse under the seat in front of her because she could have it in her lap. As soon as the attendants were done, they made their way to front of the plane and the cake-faced attendant performed the safety procedure demonstrations before take off.

"I don't know why they still go over this annoying lecture. They should just play it on a T.V. while we wait for boarding," Mr. Red Tie said.

Continuing to looking down at my phone, not paying any attention to the cake-faced attendant, I couldn't help but nod, showing Mr. Red Tie that I agreed with him.

"But, people wouldn't watch it and then the airlines would be heavily liable and under scrutiny because passengers would say that they didn't know what to do," I said, putting my two cents in.

"I guess you're right," Mr. Red Tie said in agreement.

As the cake-faced attendant finished her three-minute speech about flight safety, the lights turned off—along with the flowing air from above. The captain gave us a warm, static welcome over the intercom, "I want thank you all for choosing Alaska as your airline today. The weather in San Jose is eight-seven degrees with a light wind from the west.

If you are returning, welcome back. If you are visiting, enjoy the sun. I've turned on the seatbelt sign as we are about to take off. Once the light goes off, you are free to move about the cabin. Once again, thank you for boarding Alaska Airlines."

Hopefully this flight is a smooth one, I prayed.

• • • • •

"Looks like were not going to get an inflight snack or drink," a tawdry woman behind me said.[19]

Twenty-five minutes into the flight, Mr. Red Tie introduced himself—Clay—and shared that he worked in advertising. I had asked what he was doing in Nevada. Come to find out, a newfound client wanted to open a business in San Jose. Clay planned to meet with the owner to discuss options for advertising her bakery.

"What brings you to San Jose, if you don't mind me asking?" Clay asked.

"My best friend is going through a terrible breakup and needs me. That, and, I needed to get out of town for weekend—so it's a mini-vacay," I shared.

"Sounds like this weekend is going to be fun for ya!" Clay said with an assuring nod. Then, he inquired about what I do and asked other questions as though I was interviewing for a job.

The seatbelt sign went off.

Thank god! Anymore interview questions and I was

---

[19] It's only an hour, calm your tits!

gonna slap a hoe!

"If you don't mind, I'm going to race to the restroom before anyone else does," I politely told him.[20]

Clay removed himself from his seat again, letting me know I could pass with a hand gesture. As I did, he delicately placed a hand on my back. I quickly headed into the bathroom, not sure what that was all about.

"Is it me, or is this airplane shrinking?" I said to myself , closing the door behind me. The rear restroom was tiny— tinier than a port-a-potty. Taking a minute, I splashed some water in my face. If I wasn't claustrophobic before, the plane had successfully instilled that into me now. I realized Clay was hitting on me; that much had suddenly become clear.

Flirtatious signals tend to become more visible the older you get, and you rarely have to question people's motives. Wiping the rest of the water from face with a paper towel, I unlocked and opened the door to find Clay standing just outside. He quickly walked into the tiny space, shutting the door behind him and locking it.

He and I were now chest to chest.

"Ummm...what are you doing?" I asked, shocked.

"I want to kiss you but I certainly can't do that with everybody out there," Clay said.

I was right, the man in the red tie was very much playing for my team.

"And you thought it would be a good idea to do that in here?"

---

[20] There was only one bathroom and forty people on this plan. Enough said.

"Can't get away," he flirtatiously lulled. Then, Clay wrapped his hands around my waist, pressing himself firmly against me. The man had pecs of steel.

Well...fuck it. I've never made out in an airplane restroom before, so I decided to enjoy it. A very attractive man followed me, then forced his way into this very tight restroom just to kiss a stranger...who the hell does that?

Wrapping my arms around his neck—as there was no room for anywhere else—his lips softly connected with mine. He must have planned this out because he tasted like minty freshness.

My god was he a fantastic kisser![21] Soft, yet aggressive when it needed to be.

Ten minutes passed. Clay and I were in too deep to come up for air. Yet, I knew there could be another passenger right outside the door doing the pee pee dance who might get us caught.

I unwillingly pulled my lips away from his. "We have to get back to our seats."

"Five more minutes," Clay pleaded.

"I don't think so."

Clay nodded, letting me go as he unlocked the door. He cracked the door just enough to peer out and make sure no one was waiting.

There was nobody there.

"All right, I'll go first. Wait about two minutes and then leave," he said.

---

[21] Not one guy I've kissed from my past has been able to accomplish this. Satisfactory at best.

"Sounds good," I confirmed.

Clay opened the door and promptly shut it behind him. Pulling out my phone, I waited two minutes and then made my way back to 13A. The cake-faced attendant stared at me from the front of the plane.

She raised an eyebrow.

We were caught.

Tapping Clay's shoulder, he got up again and I hastily slid into my seat, hiding behind the seat in front of me.

"The attendant knows," I whispered.

Clay's eyes grew wide with shock.

"How do you know? You're positive?" he nonchalantly asked, sitting back down.

"She looked at me square in the eyes and raised an eyebrow. Pretty sure that's the international sign for *you've been caught.*"

For the remainder of the flight—until the plan landed—we kept it cool. Well...at least I did. Clay decided he wanted to play footsies with me.

As soon as the seatbelt sign went off—passengers leapt to their feet and aggressively removed their bags from the over head compartments and forced themselves into the aisle. Imagine a jammed freeway just without cars. Clay and I waited till the cabin was mostly cleared out before deplaning. My stomach twisted into knots and grew tighter the closer we got the door.

"You two have and *especially* wonderful time in San Jose," the cake-faced attendant said, her voice brimming with judgment and a stern reprimand. She raised her eyebrow at Clay and I.

Clay nodded at her while I innocently smiled.[22] At this point, I didn't care anymore. There was no sex, just some intense lip-locking action. She needed to get over herself. It made me want to go back into the restroom with Clay, do the deed, and leave a used condom with her name on it to clean up.

Back in the air conditioned airport, Clay and I headed over to the closest Starbucks. My bestie—Eve—was on her way, though it was going to take her awhile to arrive. Clay had some time to kill as well, so we ordered beverages and I got to know the person who held captive in a tiny airplane bathroom and forced me to make out.[23]

I still can't believe that a man who was taller by an inch with chocolate brown hair, piercing blue eyes, bulging biceps—a fitted shirt could barely contain them—found me attractive. I'm not complaining, but what did I have that turned him on?

Eventually, Eve texted to let me know she had arrived and was waiting in the pick up area. Clay and I hugged goodbye and I'm not gonna lie, it felt amazing to have him wrap his big, strong arms around me.

God, I miss that.

• • • • •

Night fell rather quickly, and the palm tree lined streets became with lit amber street lights.

---

[22] Really what I wanted to say was, "And you stay out of heat/humidity otherwise your gonna melt!

[23] Okay, I was willing.

Toto, I don't think we're in Kansas anymore.

I didn't realize how much I needed a change of scenery. Anymore time spent in the desert[24] and they might as well lock me up with the crazies. I'm not the biggest fan when it comes to humidity, but it didn't discourage me from having some fun.

"Hey, is there a CVS or a Walgreens near by? Just need to grab a few things before we head to the hotel," I asked Eve.

"Of course. There's a mini-mart up the road from where we're staying," Eve said with a smile.

Little did I know she would shuttle me to where graffiti littered the walls of buildings in a blink of an eye. My hand slowly crept to my door, and I pressed down on the lock.

The mini-mart she took me to didn't have what I needed. It was more of a one-stop liquor shop than anything else. Across the street, I noticed there were household items.

Jackpot!

They must have a dental care section...or so I thought.

Stepping inside, my eyes widened with astonishment. The shelves and floor were littered with random products that seemed haphazardly strewn throughout the store. But it wasn't a store, it was a third-world country.

An asian woman in nothing but a blue muumuu and white fuzzy slippers shuffled out from a room in the back of the store. She greeted us with a heavy, accented "hello" and sat down in a chair behind the register counter to watch

---

[24] Yes, Reno is in the desert.

some soap opera.

Eve and I reciprocated with a shocked hello.

Looking around, I found exactly what I needed behind a plastic case: a tiny tube of toothpaste and a toothbrush that you had to rip off from the vertical stack. Indeed, this was a third-world market I had just stepped into.

After paying for the items and getting the hell out of dodge, Eve and I met up with Kitty at the hotel. Kitty—a strawberry blonde, opinionated, wild child—has been Eve's bestie since moving back to San Jose. She was the type of girl I would make friends with instantly. As the girls finished applying last minute makeup touchups, our Uber pulled up and waited. It would soon take us to a well-known gay bar.

• • • • •

The vibrant nightlife of downtown San Jose pulsated with throngs of excited people. Lines stretched around the corner of every bar and club, including Splash, the gay bar we were heading to. Per usual, the club required and ID check to get in, accompanied by the bouncer's quick, *my job is hard* stare into my eyes until he looked back down at my ID. But, getting my picture taken right then and there was new...never had to do that before.

Looking for my girls, I found them already inside, pulling money out of an ATM. When I asked them why, Kitty turned me around and pointed. Near the bar, I saw a large black sign with white lettering that read CASH ONLY. Shaking my head, I pulled out cash as well. I figured the owner—Cheap McCheapskates—didn't wanna have to pay transaction fees, but he didn't mind if the rest of us paid ATM fees.

But that wasn't going to bring this guy down! I didn't come all this way just to let some cheap owner take away my fun!

"First round is on me, ladies!" I screamed, waving twenties in the air.

A bartender heard me from across the room and waited for the the three of us to approach the bar. Bartender Mc-Muscles was in his early twenties, and he was ripped.

"Love the beard!" he said. "What can I get the three of you?" he asked.

"Sex on the Beach," Eve said first.

"I haven't had one of those in a long time! I'll take one as well," I said.

"Make it three," Kitty added.

I smiled as I looked around the club while Bartender McMuscles prepared our drinks. The club was full of hot men as far as I could see. Single men, at that! I'm going to say it again, I'm definitely wasn't in Kansas anymore. Everyone was laughing, creating memories, and dancing—and let's not forget the incredible, danceable playlist the DJ spun.[25]

"That'll be $23," the Bartender McMuscles said.

Handing the man $40, I didn't break eye contact from the activities around me.

"Allister, do you want to head upstairs?" Kitty asked.

I turned to face her, surprised. "There's a second floor?"

---

[25] Clubs in my hometown aren't really something worth talking about.

Nodding her head, Kitty led the way with Eve and I followed behind.

The upstairs wasn't as packed as the first level, which meant one thing...easier bar access! Kitty passed the bar and the dance floor and headed out a door that granted access to an outside patio...and behold, we found the rest of the gays!

Kitty found an unoccupied table and pulled out her cigarettes, silently designating this as our spot to chill for a couple of minutes while she smoked.

"Allister, guys are staring at you," Eve said under her breath.

"Nah, they're probably judging my appearance," I shrugged off.

"No. They're giving you *sex eyes*."

Subtly, I glanced over the horde of men to see if she was exaggerating. Some instantly turned away while others met my gaze. Facing the girls again, I grinned. Eve smiled and nodded, and Kitty enjoyed her cigarette more than the conversation. The feeling of being stared at was rather enjoyable. I liked being desired again because it had been a long time.

Back downstairs and three Sex on the Beaches deep, we set out to dance the rest of the night away. Everything about Splash was ten times better than I had back home. Even the Go-Go dancers were fun to watch.

"Honey, you should go give him a dollar," Eve suggested.

"You go put a dollar in his undies," I said with a smile.

Eve put a dollar in my hand, turned me around, and

shoved me toward the attractive man who reeked of raw sex. If you bottled his sweat, gay men would wear it as cologne. The Go-Go boy saw me approaching and jumped off his wooden pedestal. He grabbed my hands and placed them on his thick pecs, slowly guiding them to his underwear. He pulled his waistband and to my surprise, revealed all of himself to me. In my experience, the Go-Gos only hinted at the goods. After placing the dollar inside, Mr. Go-Go Dancer dropped to his knees, buried his face in my crotch, and nibbled at my cock.

O.M.G. was the only thing running through my head. Behind me, I heard Eve and Kitty screaming with complete joy at the soft-core porn they witnessed. Mr. Go-Go Dancer pushed himself back to his feet, still rubbing up against me. Then, he gently kissed my neck for a few seconds. He finally pulled back, winked, and hopped back onto his man station. Stunned, I turned around and walked back to my girls, who were equally shocked.

Leaving the club before last call, Taron—Kitty's boyfriend—picked us up and drove us back the hotel room.

Then, while laying in bed with Eve, we stayed up for another hour and rehashed the night's event. Before passing out, Eve announced that we were going to have much more fun in Capitola tomorrow.

As long as there weren't Go-Gos ready and waiting to bite my dick, I was in.

July 13, 2018

Peeps,

You're the only two people I know who haven't traveled by plane yet, and you know I rarely ever do as well. I'm more of a *you come to me* type of guy. Don't get me wrong, flying is great but the whole going to another city and my over-thinking personality about every possible negative situation doesn't mix. But for whatever reason, there will be moments that my well-being needs to evacuate my hometown for a couple of days—either to San Francisco or to a nearby city. Thus, flying is not required.

Did you know there's an airport attire etiquette?

I didn't!

Tank-tops and jeans just aren't cutting it as many, many travelers have gawked in horror for what I deemed decent. My fellow gays have even turned their noses in disappointment. Chinos, a button up, and a relaxed dress shoe are the appropriate men's attire when changing time zones in the air. This means a new Pinterest board must be created to provide me the do's and don'ts when up in the clouds.

I'm writing to you letting you know this, so that in the future you two don't ever have to go through the same walk of flight shame I endured.

Always,

Allister

P.S.

Scarf down your inflight beverages as the attendants do not provide adequate snack time to enjoy your ridiculously tiny biscotti and unsweetened midget Starbucks coffee. Came really close to tackling the attendant with caked on makeup when she took away my caffeine.

P.P.S.

If you ever find yourself in the San Jose area and are thinking about heading to Capitola, heed this warning: take an Uber because there is no parking. My friends and I spent a good 20 minutes driving around in circles while looking for a parking spot.

Every time we thought one was going to open up, we were let down, causing a group "ah" to happen...a great bonding moment in Kitty's Prius. It was worth it, though. The small city and its beach were beautiful despite the extra parking effort.

To: *Allister_ at_ home*
From: *August_ at_ home*
Subject: *The Church & A Facebook Post*

August 22, 2018

Hi Allister,

So, something happened.[26]

A group from our church ward went to the DFW Temple a couple of Saturdays ago. For Mormons, temples are awesome a place to connect closely with God—and among many things, they do Baptisms for the dead there. They are super cool. So we all (25 or so) got checked in—I was given my white romper and the special white underwear. I got dunked on behalf of my dad and another relative who had passed away.

The guy who dunked me was another Priesthood holder.

Anyway, there is a locker room/restroom area right next to the baptismal font. The guy who dunked me was a 20-something; blonde, cute, not part of our church, and had driven about an hour west to work and spend the day at the temple.

In the locker room, the dressing areas are all private little

---

[26] Aw, shit!

rooms. I beelined for the one with a locking door as opposed to a curtain. I changed out of the white romper, put my suit back on, and as I stepped out of the private room, I saw the guy who dunked me.

"Thanks," I said. "Hope I wasn't giving your arm the death grip."

"No, I like coming up here. I still get nervous, though. One time, I was attempting to pronounce some primitive Native American names and I know I butchered them. I felt like such a jerk."

"Its not a big deal, could happen to anyone," I said.

Then we started talking about the church, about me being a convert, and being the only Mormon in my family. About how he was raised Mormon but his family had become inactive.

Somewhere in the middle of our conversation, I couldn't help but wonder what was going on. Maybe it's just me, but I always thought the amount of conversation between guys in a restroom setting was supposed to be limited to none at all. But, he was friendly and I wanted to be polite, so I engaged the conversation. When it seemed like we had been talking too much, I politely introduced myself (we hadn't shared names yet) and I gestured toward the door like I was about to say, "nice talking with you," and then leave. But then he sprung another question. "What kinds of things do your parents question you about?"

"Whether Joseph Smith was real."

And another question...and another...

All the while, he held open the door to the private, lockable changing room. Mind you, he had been standing halfway in the changing room, having an extended conversation with me. Now, I know there's a website called mormonboyz.-com[27], and I know there's a fetish about the special underwear and doing it in risky places. Still, I didn't think that's what his motives were with me. I am somewhat new to being around cute boys and hot men who are kind of clueless when it comes to inadvertently sending signals.

But, my brain went there. I was one only head nod away from defiling the Lord's dressing room. It'd be a great story if I said that happened...but it didn't. The funny thing is, although he was cute, I didn't do any double takes or check him out previously. He didn't turn my head until he held a genuine conversation...one where we quickly talked about personal things, for me and for him. We bonded.

So, I left the dressing room and found the sister missionaries I drove down with were ready to go. I thought about him the whole drive home. It made me wonder; was it really

---

[27] I've been to that site and President Faust is my favorite! TMI, I know...but I don't care.

about sex (and being horny) or was it about intimacy? The conversation and the setting were intimate...that's what got my head going (both of them.) I didn't have any sexual thoughts previously.

Who knows, maybe I will see him again on some future Saturday. A good friendship would be better for me at this stage of my life.

Hope you are well, and that the book tour is going great.

Talk to you later,

August

==

To: *August_at_home*
From: *Allister_at_home*
Subject: RE: *The Church & The Facebook Post*

August 25, 2018

Dear August,

The special underwear is a real thing!

I always thought it was just a myth, something created to add a bit of mystery when discussing Mormon guys. And now, my curiosity has been fulfilled. Haha. You are correct when it comes to men and locker rooms/restrooms as they're very intimate and a vulnerable area, probably why women treat it as a place of sanctuary when personal matters become topic—that, and passing tampons under the stalls. It's very odd that he would want to strike a conversation in that type of setting. Maybe he could be gay himself and wants to get to know who Jason is and what he's all about? Was there any sort of vibe there?

But, I am proud of you for composing yourself while in a place of faith. You never know, maybe sometime in the near future you two will cross paths yet again under a different setting—one that doesn't have toilets and urinal cakes in the background.

My first stop for my book tour is on the 28th my hometown. Apparently, the assistant store manager had to order another shipment of books as the first order had already sold out, which is great to hear!

Even though it's August and a small town, Reno puts on Pride at the end of the month. I've been invited to attend the annual Mayor's Pride Party later that day. Never been before, and I'm not sure what to expect from it. I haven't been in the gay scene for quite some time. There are individuals I choose not to come into contact with.

But, with the severe Midwest manners my mother instilled in me, one can be cordial and treat it as such without any form of ill will.

Here's hoping for the best.

Always,

Allister

———————————————————————————————

4

#MayorMadeMeDoIt

"That looks great, guys!" the club owner gleefully said.

Taking a deep breath so I wouldn't say something caddy,[28] I continued to arrange fruit slices and grapes around the chocolate fountain. I'm still not sure what's so exoteric about the gay bar Faces. Yeah, it maybe bigger—space wise, but when you have tacky red velvet oblong couches trailing up to the dance floor, cyclopean mirrors on the walls, and long dark drapes in random locations you might as well have stepped into The Birdcage. Though that all-star cast movie is one for the books and I'm in no way dogging it, this club was just a cheap imitation. At least he could have made the evening's party decorations flare. A tower of

---

[28] If you think a decadent fruit display surrounding a fountain of chocolate looks great, then what looks like shit to you?

glasses filled champagne, maybe?

"As a special thank you, there will be bottle service for the two of you," the club owner added.

"Thank you," Gary said, appreciating the kind gesture.

Out of politeness, I nodded at the club owner, piggy-backing off Gary's gratitude.

A few weeks prior, Gary invited me to accompany him just before my trip to San Jose. He's one of the most respected gays in the community[29] to the point that when he steps into a room people automatically stop what their doing—even those in mid-conversation—just to come say hi an get an updated run-down on each others' lives.[30] Fortuitously, when people came up to him they didn't know who the hell I was because my beard shielded my identity until Gary introduced me to people I already knew. Each and every one of them greeted me with a warm fake welcome, but I knew judgment was being passed. I was hoping to stay in the *witness beard protection program* during this event.

Gary plugged in the fountain and poured the melted chocolate into the bowl, a little bit a time, until it overflowed from the top. Then a fun idea popped into his head.

"Hey, so I have fun drinking game we can play tonight," Gary said.

"What's your idea?" I quizzically asked.

"Basically, we take a drink every time whenever Mr.

---

[29] Just a brief bio; a 50 year-old late bloomer who was married to lady, has children, is now making up for lost gay time, and is one of the gay community's biggest gossip queens. He claims I bring drama, yet has no problem sharing others dirty laundry.

[30] Kind of like how one gay—one I won't mention—uses Facebook to friend request people only to stalk and spread gossip. Thanks for the heads up, Gary.

Ego[31] refers to the mayor as his best friend and refers to his partner as 'my Joey,'" Gary suggested with a smile.

"Sounds like an interesting game. Does Mr. Ego really introduce the mayor as his best friend?"

"Yeah, he does."

"Didn't they just announce on Facebook they're officially in a relationship? It's a little too early for calling a partner 'my Joey,'" I said. "I doubt he'll do any of what you said."

"So it's a deal?" Gary asked.

"Sure," I replied.

Gary giggled and finished up with the chocolate fountain, making sure it wasn't going to breakdown or cause any issues during the event. Then he offered to buy the first round of cocktails.

• • • • •

Later that evening and five cosmopolitans in, the once empty bar had filled with high-society gays, which meant those who couldn't drop $50 dollars at the door moved on to next gay bar down the road. Fifty dollars in drinks out weighs a fifty dollar ticket any day...or should I say any Saturday night. Ugh, the struggles of being a twenty-something

---

[31] Another respected gay in the community who always needs to be in the spotlight or stay relevant. Case in point, he integrated himself into an investigation about a gay kid who was found along the train tracks. Mr. Ego ended up on the front page of the newspaper because of his "efforts" toward the kid.

gay![32]

Word got around that Mayor Schieve was about to arrive. That news created an avalanche of people at the bar who ordered another round of drinks and casually headed to the dance floor where strategically placed tables were slowly filling up. Gary whispered that a table was reserved for us up front, and that since we would be sharing with Mr. Ego and his boyfriend, there was no need to rush.

Is this what being privileged feels like?

VIP bottle service, reserved seating, having people brown nose you to the point of coming off as pathetic. A few gays even called me Daddy out of nowhere.

Mr. Ego and his San Francisco boyfriend arrived before the mayor. Both were dressed in collared shirts, slacks, and dress shoes. Hours prior, they were trolling around the Pride grounds in nothing but underwear, dressed as purple-glittered unicorns. For someone trying to make a difference in the gay community, he seemed to create a bad image after being featured on the news. Even my own mother—who had texted me earlier—saw his news interview and was disgusted with what he was wearing. "He needs to grow up,"

---

[32] That age bracket mirrors a third-world country. I can picture it now; instead of a woman asking for donations, an older bear takes her place and surrounds himself with struggling gays who cannot afford decent cocktails. "A dollar a day can help these twinks have a healthy bar life." Sally Struthers anyone?

she said.

As with Gary, people stopped to greet Mr. Ego, who ate up every bit of publicity he could as he strolled across the dance floor and onto the stage. Last time I checked, this was about the mayor and not him, but this event was probably his idea from the get go. With the lights dimmed and the music low, Mr. Ego opened the event with a speech.

"I just want thank everyone for coming tonight to support Reno Gay Pride and now the Mayor's Pride Party. It was awesome to see everyone come together today. For me, Pride means we're here and not going anywhere."

A bunch of bullshit.

I wonder how much of his own crap he believes?

"I want to thank my partner for coming down from San Francisco to attend this event," Mr. Ego said pointing in Joey's direction as a spotlight shined on Joey.[33]

Last time I checked—and Facebook can back me up— Mr. Ego and Joey had only been dating for two weeks and using the word *partner* is premature. Partner should only be used when the two of you have said, "I do." Other than that, the only label Mr. Ego should have used was boyfriend or due to his age, *man friend*. Besides, said boyfriend didn't choose to attend this event—Mr. Ego made him come. Who in their right mind would want to leave San Francisco to attend a mediocre party. Hell, I'd never leave the bay area and judging from Joey's personality, he wouldn't have either.

---

[33] Is this why Mr. Ego's relationships don't last very long? Does he not understand how much pressure he places on the men he dates? Well, amongst other things.

Gary pulled the mayor toward us as soon as she was close enough, made rather quick introductions, then posed for a photo. Upon meeting her, I determined she was a very outgoing yet very soft-spoken conservative republican.[34]

"The time has come to honor the person we have all gathered to support, our amazing Mayor, Hilary Schieve."

A small chant grew amongst my fellow gays, Hilary...Hilary...Hilary...Hilary. The mayor excused herself from our mini-conversation and made her way onto the stage, waving and smiling as people smiled and patted her on the shoulder. It reminded me of a beauty queen relinquishing her crown to the next winner.[35] What I found to be hilarious about the entire situation was that most of the occupants were democrats who rooted for the elephant in the room. Not being one for politics, I was under the impression that you support your own kind. Am I wrong? Another reason why politics and I don't mix...they're too damn confusing if you ask me.

Once in the spotlight and after everyone quieted down, she began her speech about how much Pride had grown and that she was very proud to be a part of it. Folks around me slowly checked out and carried on their own conversations, which the mayor was not having.

"Hey! Quiet down everyone. #mayormademedoit," Hilary snapped.

I wasn't sure why she needed to include the hashtag

---

[34] Yes, I understand she's a public figure. I just don't like masked people, especially when meeting you for the first time.

[35] Local elections are coming up this November. There may be a slim chance her reign will come to an end.

when telling everyone to shut their traps, but no one took it to heart as chuckling replaced the talking. I would have been a little more abrupt about it—that's just me.

"It's time to give the Pride Award![36]"

Mayor Schieve handed the microphone back to Mr. Ego, who stepped forward. He was poised to present the award to a family member of someone who recently had a tragic moment in his life.

"You have got to be kidding me," I murmured.

"We are presenting the Pride Award to Aaron Salazar. He is the gay man who was found unconscious by the train tracks and in bad shape. The City of Reno stills wants the authorities to conduct a proper investigation, but they refuse to do so. This was clearly a hate crime and we want justice for Aaron. On behalf of Aaron, his mother and grandmother are here to accept his award," Mr. Ego compassionately announced.

Aaron's family, now on stage and fighting back tears, accepted the medal. His grandmother made a very small speech that basically thanked everyone for their support as they continued to fight for justice.

Hate crime?

I had been following this story since the beginning and nothing added up. Yes, he was found by the train tracks and they concluded that he had been thrown off the platform of a train. Yet, other passengers and train workers never saw anyone with Aaron. Medical officials stated that his genitals were burned but his pants had no scorch marks. The young

---

[36] Dumb.

man was traveling from Colorado (where Aaron attended college) back to Nevada. Grandma stated that she received a call from her grandson in a very scared tone, like he wanted to come back home. My thoughts about the situation are this: the investigation needs to start back in Colorado. Something happened there before he got on the train, and that's where investigators will find the truth. Mr. Ego and everyone else think it was a hate crime just because Aaron is gay.

I feel for Aaron, but I think it's going to be fairly awkward once the truth of what really happened is out in the open.

Mr. Ego finished up the speeches by thanking everyone for attending once again. By that time, people were already crowding around the bar to replenish their empty cocktails. The bar owner and a few volunteers helped clear the tables off the dance floor for those who want to grind to the music.

Gary and I headed back to one of the ugly red velvet couches where the promised bottle service was waiting for us along with several of his drag queen friends who I feel leech off those who are treated with VIP services. They were already helping themselves to our bottle service.

After sitting down, I observed each and every person around me, noticing how the older drag queens were being extra caddy with the younger ones. Then, I saw Isaac, who tried to hide in the corner after he realized I was there.[37] My

[37] After discovering the truth of how poor he really is during my Brutally Bitter year, he now keeps a low profile. My Sherlock Holmes traits outed him and the lies he told.

lion (an old hookup flame, the best sex I ever had) wasn't in drag, but rather all dressed up and ignoring me per usual. Gary had confirmed everything that I wondered about my lion: He's in love with a man who isn't in love with him. And if my lion tried to be monogamous with him, his partner would leave him right then and there. So, he'd rather be unhappy than be alone.

Then, I saw Adrian. We hadn't talked since his drunk confession about his brother who raped him, taking his virginity. That was over a year ago, and Adrian had since immersed himself in the drag scene, creating the drag persona[38] Sharpay[39]. He and my lion have grossly bonded during that time.[40] Sharpay purposely sat herself next to me, ready to strike up a conversation.

"How are you, Allister?" Adrian (Sharpay) asked.

"I'm well, thank you. And yourself?" I politely replied.

"Doing good!"

"Glad to hear that, Adrian."

"It's Sharpay," she said, correcting me.

"No, it's Adrian. You're only doing this because you couldn't fit in anywhere else in the gay community. So, Adrian...you are simply a boy in a dress," I abrasively told him.

A few of the other queens heard our conversation, but they turned a blind eye. Adrian opened his mouth to say something but nothing came out. Instead, he got up,

---

[38] He's not a very good looking drag queen.

[39] Sharpie is more like it.

[40] Gary filled me in that Adrian made it his mission to be relevant at all times, causing much unnecessary drama.

smoothed out his dress, and walked away.

Smartest thing I've ever seen him do.

Gary asked if everything was okay. I assured him it was but that it was time for me to go. I thanked him for inviting me out. Everything about this night was what I expected it to be: fake and drama-filled. Hugging Gary goodbye, I made my way through the club to the door but stopped when I felt a tap on my shoulder.

Turning around, I saw Mike greeting me with a smile. We had ended out friendship months ago, after the lies Connor told.

"Hey Allister, I didn't recognize you with the beard. How have you been?" Mike asked.

"I'm doing good thanks, how are you?" I responded, exercising politeness despite my conversation with Sharpay.

"You're different," Mike said, smiling.

Different? How?

Just behind Mike, Connor eavesdropped on our conversation, all the while trying not make eye contact with me. Connor ruined some of my friendships in past. Come to find out, he'd been telling lies and brainwashing my friends so he could have them all to himself.

"I'm doing well," Mike continued. "I quit my job over at Costco and I just got back from Burning Man. I would love to share my experience with you over coffee," Mike said.

"Too be honest, I'd be disinterested in that topic. Doesn't mean that someone else wouldn't enjoy hearing about it," I said.

Mike is the type of guy who is all about spiritual conquests of any sort. But, he'd rather force one than let it come naturally. Since it was at Burning Man, he probably tripped on drugs.

I fake-smiled. "Anyways, I'm heading out. Enjoy the party. I know the whore behind you will get you drunk and sleep with you if he hasn't tried to already," I loudly added.

Connor heard what I said about him, but acted like it didn't faze him. Knowing Mike is all about sharing hugs before two people go their separate ways, I gave him a good pat on the shoulder, like a parent to a child, and walked away before anything else could be said.

"Door...Door...Door," I said under my breath.

Out of the corner of my eye, I saw a figure in white approaching me from the side. Knowing who it was without turning to face them, I rushed out the door.

It was my lion.

He was most likely drunk and filled with enough liquid courage to hold a meaningless conversation with me. He wasn't going to get the chance. If he's got something to say, he needs to figure it out on his own. I had my fill for the night and didn't need anymore screen time for *Gays of Our Lives*.

Blame the beard. Drives men to do crazy things.

11. MEET THE MAYOR

August 28, 2018

Hey Girls.

So, it happened.

It came out of nowhere. Had no warning whatsoever. The best pair of jeans I've ever owned—you know the ones that make my booty pop—finally decided to give up. Too much booty to contain, I'm guessing. They ripped in the corners of the back pockets. Devastation is the best word to describe how I'm feeling right now.

The funeral was beautiful. I folded them as though they were a brand new pair sitting on the display table in a store and walked outside to the garbage can that truly is a garment coffin. Said a few words, placed them inside, and closed the lid.

It's garbage day—so, the goodbye was quick.

Always,

Allister

5

French Lesson

"Let's have a basic conversation," Paul said.

I received online classes—thanks to my grandma—in learning to speak french. I already speak Norwegian, so I figured I might as well get another language under my belt. Paul is a British man who speaks the love language rather fluently. I would have never guessed he was from the UK.

"Salute, Allister," Paul starts.

"Salute, Paul, Comment ça va?" I responded.

"Bién merci, et toi?

"Je vais très bien," I said.

Even though Paul was only a voice on my computer, he sounded pretty pleased I was able to pick up a simple conversation quickly. My teacher decided that he was going to see if I was really paying attention...

"Comment vous appelez-vous?"

"Je m'appelle Allister" I responded.

"Tres bien!"

"Est-ce que vous parlez français?" Paul added.

"Oui, je parle français," I said.

And here I believed French was going to be rather difficult.

303

Andrew Christian,

I have some beef with you.

Even though your underwear maybe cute,[41] I'm not finding it difficult to toss every pair I've purchased into the garbage. The first time I met you—which was at a rundown bar claiming to be a club—one of my questions during the interview was, "How do you want men to feel when wearing your designs?" Your response was simple: "Sexy." Little did I know then that your product had an expiration date on "sexy."

Putting on your solid heather grey pouched-briefs the other day, the pair with the red, yellow, and blue strips on the side, made me feel so desperate to remain twenty-something *attraction* now that I'm over the gay hill of thirty. Especially when the size mediums really feel like an extra small slowly creeping into my ass crack transforming themselves into a thong.

Tight and uncomfortable quickly comes to mind. I believe what you meant was "sexy for two-seconds until they end up on the floor." Is that why there's a pouch? Advertising to those who are seeking? It's all starting to make sense to me now; the underwear with the pouch is for tops and the jock-

---

[41] Which only seems to be cute on gay pornstar models, odd.

straps ones also known as "Trophy Boy" are meant for bottoms. So, I have to ask myself—do I want come across classy or easy?

Hmm... Something about wanting a guy to see me as potential husband material rather than a one night stand has me non-regrettably swiping my credit card over at Macy's for Calvin Klein or Armani square cut trunk undies. At least their sizing is true and never disappoints.

I totally understand where your design aesthetic stands. Why should women everywhere get all the fun? Suggestion? May I propose a branch that gives men of a mature nature—as I'm one of many who no longer circles the first age bracket on paperwork—the feeling, as you say, of being "sexy" without giving off a mid-life crisis vibe. Think Victoria's Secret. They have their PINK store for younger ladies and the regular store for mature woman.

But, like I said, I have no problem tossing your underwear in the garbage.

Always,

Allister

To: *Allister_at_home*
From: *August_at_home*

Subject: *New Place*

September 4, 2018

Hey Allister,

Hope all is well—love that gym shirt you had on FB.

So, I moved this weekend. I love my new place and community. Still putting away boxes and using this as an attempt to declutter. I got a phone call Saturday. One of the Brothers from the Priesthood asked if I could meet with The Bishop after Sunday services. I said okay. Truth be told, after three hours of church I usually want out, but I'll never say no. So I'm left wondering what the deal is going to be.

After services, the Bishop starts off by asking me what's been going on and how I've been doing. I give the small talk answer of, "Fine. Moving. Keeping busy," he continues, "The reason I wanted to talk to you. On Facebook, you're friends with members of the church and there was a post that cause concern, about you coming out at 16."

I was instantly dumbfounded trying to think of what he was talking about. Because of my line of work and that I am friends with my grandma etc., I am very careful of what I post on my feed. I try to be a no politics, no controversy or divisiveness, kind of guy. I often hide friends' postings because I have to be logged onto Facebook for work and the last thing I want showing is some screenshot from what looks like a gay porn.

After some confusion over whether it was a Facebook post or a text message, I remembered what it was. I'm going to Utah after Reno next month. I had heard there is a whole subculture of Mormon men who identify as gay (or SSA as some call it) but they are married to women, who know, and they have kids and are much happier. They don't practice being gay anymore but they also don't suppress it or are closeted about it. I'm not saying, "sign me up for that" so much as I am saying, "I'd be interested in learning more."

So, in doing my research I found these groups (which are not like old school electrocute-you-reparative-therapy groups) have a presence online. I joined a public Facebook group and posted the below question. I couldn't remember exactly what I said when I was with the Bishop because I was so nervous. He said, "Probably more people saw this than you intended." He shared with me that, "We have re-sources here in Texas, so you don't have to go all the way to Utah for that. And as long as it's thoughts and not actions there's no problem." In other words, "be gay all day long if that's your thing but don't act it out." He then said a prayer where he discussed the adversary's fiery darts that come our way and that was that. I walked out of the meeting not feel-ing bad at all.

But I immediately went to Facebook in my car, found the post, and didn't think it was bad at all. There's nothing wrong with it. I double checked to make sure it did not go out on my newsfeed—and it didn't. However, it was a public group, meaning someone purposefully went to the groups on my Facebook page, clicked on the group, saw the post, and got concerned. It's not as if someone came across it. That's different for me.

It left me wondering if I should be mad about this. Usually the answer to that question is "no." If you're on the fence about whether to feel negative, choose positivity instead. They were just trying to let me know resources are available here, too. But I keep going back to "someone snooped your page, and found reason to be concerned and tattled to the Bishop.

What do you think?

August

To: *August_at_home*
From: *Allister_at_home*
Subject: *New Place Response*

September 5, 2018

Dear August,

Congrats on the new place! Usually when moving, I use that time to declutter as well and throw out what I don't need anymore.

Reading your post, I don't think you were in the wrong at all. They said you can be gay all you want, but just don't have sex. Well, you weren't having sex. I wouldn't take what they say into consideration. As far as someone snooping your posts, I don't think this is the case. It sounds like posting in the wrong group. I would be posting in a group that none of your church colleagues are a part of, that way you can stay safely anonymous and be yourself without any further consequence.

Honestly, that just pisses me off! Cleary they said don't act upon it physically, and yet it was just words. Before they open up and tell you what is wrong, an understanding of what they are saying to you needs to be comprehended. It's just baffling. You did nothing wrong, stand behind you post!

Apparently, at the last store I visited for my book tour, the store manager emailed me and told me my book has sold out. They had at least ten left—out of 70—remaining. I was pretty pleased to hear that! Wish me luck!

Always,

Allister

6

Urbandictionary.com

As gym law states, *"Though Shall Have One Cheat Day A Week."* I take full advantage of it by treating myself to In-N-Out Burger. I don't give a damn about the health risks the paper-wrapped burger provides; it's just too good not to give up.

After placing my order, I rolled to the first window to pay for my greasy lunch. A young twenty-something guy with diamond-studded pierced ears opened the window and I instantly felt shy. Gayby alert! And, of course, he checked me out.

"You ordered the Double-Double meal animal style?" he asked, confirming my order.

"Correct," I replied.

"$11.97."

"A bit expensive, but it beats McDonald's any day," I said.

Handing over my debit card, the gayby initiated small talk.

"How are you today?" he asked.

"Starving!" I responded with a smile, "How are you?"

"Straightlined."

The gayby handed back my card and wished me a wonderful rest of my day with a flirtatious smile.[42] I, on the other hand, had no idea what the hell he just said to me, but I smiled back anyway. It's official...I'm no longer current with the times! Searching online as I slowly rolled up the second window, I knew urbandictionary.com[43] would be the site to answer my burning question.

And boy did it!

According to the site, straightlined is thusly defined: Similar to the 'Hot Carl' sexual maneuver, where one partner defecates in the other's mouth. E.G. - Brent straightlined his domestic partner Brad.[44]

Jaw-dropped by what I just read, I wondered if the gayby even knew what he said? Apparently, you can do a lot on a fifteen-minute break. I just hope that kid has Listerine on hand at all times...and maybe some gum wouldn't hurt, too.

A chipper young girl waited for me at the second window. She asked me how I was doing and confirmed my order as well.

---

[42] More like a come fuck me smile.

[43] The only thing keeping me in the loop of pop culture.

[44] It's like the HUMAN CENTIPEDE all over again.

"I'm a bit taken back by what your fellow coworker said to me," I admitted.

"What do you mean?" she asked, tilting her head. Holding out my phone so she could read what was on the screen, her jaw dropped as well.

"I do apologize for that. He will be spoken to about it."

"Be kind," I said. "He's young and the hormones are raging and begging to come out."

She didn't know what to say, so she shoved my lunch into my hand and told me to have good day. Kids these days just don't appreciate sarcastic humor.

And this is the future people of America...serious, straightlined Americans.

To: *Eve_at_home, Kitty_at_home,*
From: *Allister_at_home*
Subject: *The Girl With The Apology*

September 10, 2018

Hey Loves,

Today, out of the blue, I received a Facebook message from someone I haven't spoken to in over three years, apologizing for what she did. Before I get into it, a backstory is needed.

Serendipity and I met as coworkers many moons ago. The same one I met Eve at—you remember girl? She and I grew very close and before I knew it, we were best friends drinking wine on any lazy afternoon. The cool thing about it was that we had the same days off. One day I would be over at her place drinking wine with her, and other days she would be at mine doing the same thing.

Do you remember the empty bottles of wine I had on display up above the cupboards? Some were drank by us. I believe you've actually met her, Jackie. She was at birthday wine tasting party. We did everything together! I took her Gay Pride cherry, was there when she gave birth to her second child, and watched her children while she was getting a boob job. Any-who, when everything between Richard (the ex who attacked me and got away with it) and I happened, she still needed me to attend her bachelorette party in

Tahoe. During that time, I was not in the best mindset and was recovering from a broken hand. "Drinking and depression isn't exactly the best combination," I told her. Yet, she didn't care, she still demanded I be there even though none of her other bridesmaids showed up for her dress fittings, helped her plan every little detail, and was up at seven in the morning driving all the way to a little town in California supporting her while she got her save the date photos taken.

I understand the bridezilla complex, but this is beyond that. She and I said some very hurtful things to one another we didn't mean. Nonetheless, she reached out and apologized for what she had done. The thing is, I've spent the past year apologizing to individuals that I was nasty to all because of the bitterness I exerted. In return, none of them gave me a second chance and ran off with my apology.

In our conversation today, she confessed wanting to reach out earlier this year because she needed a friend after being roofied and raped. She wasn't conscious during the unfortunate event, but medical professionals confirmed her worst fears. I'm a little upset and angry Serendipity had to go through that and would have stopped what I was doing to be the friend she needed regardless of what happened between us in the past. If any of you were going through something like that, you know I would be on the first flight out!

I'm a very forgiving person and will always allow friends to redeem themselves if they've wronged to me, though I've never received that. I'm willing to give Destinee that second chance.

The question I'm asking the two of you is...do you think it's a mistake?

Always,

Allister

7

Elle & Carrie
Reunited

Three years.

That's how long it took for Serendipity and I to start talking again. She never received the letter I'd sent months ago, but she was a point in her life where she needed her best friend back. We had decided to meet at the Cheesecake Factory for cocktails and lunch.

Serendipity hadn't changed one bit; Curly black hair, skinny as ever, and titties like no other. Her personality was as bubbly as a freshly opened Champagne bottle.

"We've been fighting long enough and it's become dumb. I miss being able to talk to you about everything," Serendipity expressed.

"I have to agree. I let go of everything that has happened between us months ago. I've missed you as well. Hope the space has allowed the both of us to heal and move on under a different light," I said.

"The time has flown and I really miss your company," Serendipity said, starting to cry. "I wanted to tell you so badly, but we were fighting and I let my pride blind me. So, I dealt with on my own." The conversation became serious, and we talked about her rape incident, "Scariest shit of my life. Felt so dirty and stupid. They never found the guy."

"You should have messaged me on Facebook. Our fight would have become water under the bridge and I could have been there for you," I conveyed to her.

After ordering our first round of Cosmopolitans, she spilled how it happened.

"It all went down at Tub Tubs. I was with my husband and his two friends. An hour before midnight—roughly—my husband and one of his friends headed outside while the other and myself stayed at the bar. I told the friend I was using the restroom and if he could grab our drinks when they came back, which he did. From there, I don't remember anything except for waking up in a clinic for those who have been raped."

Sighing in utter disbelief, the one detail worth questioning was the fact that if she didn't know she was raped, how the hell did her husband know?

"How did they find you?" I asked.

"They told me I walked up to them acting like a zombie and I wasn't responding. That's when they dragged me out of the bar," Serendipity said, gulping her cosmo.

"Sweetie. The guy who did this to you is either your husband or one of the two friends. My assumption is one of the two friends. If I had found you like that, the hospital would have been the place to take you, not a rape clinic. The hospital would have made that assessment right then and there. One of them wanted to have sex with you and confessed his desire to your husband. This was a way for them—including you husband—to make it happen," I expressed.

Serendipity's face drained of color as she sank back in her chair.

"I don't mean to cause any..."

"No, No! You're the only person who has made sense in all this. It's most logical actually," she said.

"What are you going to do?"

"For starters, divorce[45] that fucking piece of shit! From there, I don't know."

"Well, you're not alone anymore," I told her.

She reached for my hand and clenched hard, "I'm sorry I fucked up our friendship."

There is was, the three words I needed her to say. Serendipity meant the apology and it didn't feel hollow to me. Sometimes, it takes a traumatic experience to understand someone else's. Looking past my strong, beautiful friend, I signaled our waitress for another round—we were going to need it.

---

[45] From the first day I've met her and husband, deep down I knew they weren't meant to be. It's hard to accept that it took something like this to make her see that.

To: *August_at_home*
From: *Allister_at_home*
Subject: *a BIG decision*

September 21, 2018

Dear August,

Something has been brought to my attention!

Nothing too extreme, but it's one that needs a decision rather quickly and I feel that you can provide me some insight.

A male friend—Sawyer—who has been in my life for five years brought up his very own bucket list. Now, before I tell you what that list consists of, he and I have mutual feelings for each other. We haven't seen each other in a very long time, but we do stay in contact via email, text, and phone calls. Now, I know you understand Bradshaw lingo when I say that this man is BIG. He's one of those guys with a big personality you notice as soon as he walks into the room. In the words of Bradshaw, "When that big love comes along, it's not always easy. No one was ever quite big enough." Something about him is different than another guy I've met. I've never told anyone this before.

Here's what his list is: a sex bucket list. As it turns out, he only wants to do it with me and yet, we haven't had sex. At the end of the month, I will be attending Folsom Street Fair

—an annual event where a couple of streets are blocked off in San Francisco allowing those of the leather culture to flourish. Not sure if you knew that or not. One of the reasons he is attending this event with me and my girls—Eve and Kitty—is because I was supposed to attend his annual camping trip and at the last minute, I had to bail. Eve needed me more. So, I owe him.

The problem I'm seeing is this: do I attempt to help him check something off his bucket list—and only his list—or do I just continue my sexless one?

Always,

Allister

═══════════════════════════════

To: *Allister_at_home*
From: *August_at_home*
Subject: *a BIG decision—Response*

September 23, 2018

Hi Allister,

Hope your weekend is going well. It's 9 p.m. here and I've been in bed since 8 p.m., filling in on an overnight shift tonight. We are short people and I write the schedule, decided it was my turn, and since I'm salaried, so much for OT. Wishing I could fall asleep! I know all about Folsom St. I have never been, but I got some wildness out of my system in New Orleans and NYC back in the day.

Maybe try non-sexual intimate stuff, like spend the night without sex? Intimacy is hot, and it always makes me horny. If you both decide to do more you'll have previously grown closer which makes it better. Easy for me to say, though. Before I quit drinking, though, my response would have been for both of us to get drunk and rip off our clothes for a wild time.

Either way, enjoy the moment! Let me know how it goes!

August

To: *August_at_home*
From: *Allister_at_home*
Subject: *a BIG decision—RE:Respone*

September 24, 2018

Dear August,

I have a few days to think about it before this upcoming

leather weekend in San Francisco. My girls—Kitty & Eve—will be joining me, along with Kitty's boyfriend and Eve's friend Lucy. There'll be six of us all together. Sawyer wants to us to be more than friends. He feels that I would understand his bucket list and that's why he only wants to complete it with me.

Our chemistry plays a big factor in that, which I can understand. Last week on the phone, he was explaining what he was looking for and why he's been single for so long. Sawyer had confessed that long ago he did find his partner. They had been together for five years, but their time was cut short as the partner committed suicide.

Sawyer refrained from going into deeper detail after that. The way he described him and their relationship was like watching *The Notebook*. A fairytale love like that is hard to find and leaves very big shoes to fill if the chemistry between us ends up being better than expected. We'll have to see what happens in San Francisco.

Always,

Allister

8

Monarch Mess

"We only accept debit or credit cards that have chips," a short middle eastern woman said.

Looking down at the card reader, I saw the part where you swipe the card was covered by a long blue strip of painter's tape. The front desk woman subtly threw her hands up, showing that there was no other way to complete the check-in. Luckily, I had a different card that fit the hotel's requirements. As a precaution years ago, I opened two accounts from different banks. Smart, but the only problem was that there was only two hundred in that account.

"It would've been nice to know that before I drove four hours," I told her, irritated.

"I understand, but I don't make the rules," she said.

It's a cop-out response in my mind. Silently flipping out, I asked where the closest bank was. She gave cut and dry directions of where to go—even offered to watch my bags, leaving them behind the front desk while I corrected this minor infraction.[46]

"There's always Motel 6 down the road if it's a problem," the middle eastern woman offered.

Shaking my head no, my internal freakout became more of a mental breakdown now. All I wanted to do is jst take a shower, relax for a hot second, and grab some dinner.

Walking out the front door and using the directions she gave me, I navigated the homeless-infested streets of San Francisco quickly before the banks closed as it was nearing five in the afternoon. Good thing my main bank was right around the corner; I could get in, withdraw the money, and get out. My other bank though, was seven blocks away, and if I didn't get the money deposited, Motel 6 would be calling my name

---

[46] Does this happen to anyone else or is it just me? I'm in the capital for fuck sake! Can I get a break?

—and who knows what awaits there?[47]

Now running, I sprinted passed people walking the opposite direction—apologizing profusely when I bumped into them. San Francisco humidity wasn't doing me any justice, and at this point, my body shimmered with a light layer of sweat. Then my phone rang...

"Hello?" I said, breathy.

"Hey, honey," Eve sweetly said.

"Sweetie, I need to call in you about ten minutes, I'm a little pissed off at the moment and need to get the hotel shit fixed!"

"All right, I'm just letting you know I'm heading your way," She said.

"See you soon!" I delicately responded.

Shit!—Eve's going to get here and there won't be a hotel room waiting for her!

• • • • •

Hustling back to the Monarch Hotel after successfully transfering the money between banks, I checked in and was assigned to room 510.[48] The Monarch was dated to the point where they converted a decent sized closet to an elevator. The wooden door didn't open automatically and the interior was constructed with nothing but plywood. I wasn't sure if that was up to code or not. Stepping into the death trap, I headed up.

---

[47] If ended up there, I am wrapping everything in plastic!

[48] Not today Satan! Motel 6 can just suck it!

Apparently, nobody here likes sunlight as the window shades has been drawn closed. A dark grey plum color covered all the walls that were lined with white crown molding. To the right of the elevator was a steep narrow staircase lined with hideous black carpet—yes, dated at best. I found room 510 around the corner. Swiping the card, a little green light appeared on the handle. I entered the room, dropped my bags after the door shut, and collapsed on one of the double beds.

Laying on my back, I scoped out the room and noticed two things: large bay windows and a cyclopean closet—big enough to hold a blow up mattress. This room was about to host six people, but the two double beds were only going to fit two people in each of them. This is how the bed situation would go down...

Tonight: Eve and Luke arrive. Eve gets her own bed, Luke and I will share the other.

Saturday: Lucy, Kitty, Taron arrive. Eve and Lucy take a bed, Kitty and Taron take the other bed. I'll take the blow up mattress with Sawyer.

Sunday Night: Everyone leaves except for Sawyer. He and I will have the room to ourselves.

Monday: Leave.

Complicated, yes.

9

Mantrum Like
No Other

"What's happening with dinner?" Kitty asked.

"Well, Sawyer pushed back our dinner reservations to 6:30, so we now have a bit more time. It's at Tu Lan instead of where we were going at Fishermans Wharf," I said, looking at everyone around the room.

Eve and Lucy sighed in relief as they were no where close to being ready and turned back to mirror to finish their hair and makeup. At this point, I had become quite upset with how the day progressed—other than champagne at Tiffany's. Sawyer ditched us at the hotel so he could do god knows what in the Castro. When he was with us, he put no effort into showing me any kind of affection. Weeks before, we both were excited about this trip—we could finally figure out if we could be more than friends. A subtle gesture would have sufficed. Instead, I put in way too much effort—once again—into something that obviously wasn't there.

Sawyer was either too worried about shopping or fawning over the freakishly hot singer in front of the mall performing covers/original songs and tried to cozy up to him by offering his PR/Marketing services or his charger.

My phone dinged, and it was from the man himself. He had sent me a photo of the Mr. S-Leather event and included a small blurb.

"Got a VIP ticket...well, just for myself."[49]

I sighed in utter disbelief. There's six of us total, and he managed to procure a single VIP ticket for himself.

What the hell?

Fucking selfish if you ask me.

The more I thought about last 24 hours, Sawyer was not the guy I thought him to be. The more we hung out, the more I became disinterested in him as a potential boyfriend—or even a friend.

By 6:20, everyone was ready—including the Uber car Taron requested. The gang looked like a million bucks! Eve wore a yellow blazer with black high waisted sailor shorts. Kitty wore a velvet emerald green jumpsuit giving off mermaid chic. And I wore what I normally wear when not in San Fran—skinny jeans, a pair of brown boots, a blue button up, and a burgundy cardigan. I looked like fifty bucks—

[49] Strike Two

probably what this entire outfit cost all together.

Heading out the door, Eve and Kitty noticed one of the housekeeping closets was open, and that it held more blankets, pillows, and bathroom essentials where the girls began to raid and stashed the loot back in the room for later.[50] Telling the them to hurry, I went down the narrow staircase, nearly tripping on the carpet.

Outside, a black Escalade waited for us to climb in. Taron and Lucy were already inside, waving us down. The driver was a young twenty-something guy wearing a green sweater and a white collared button up.[51]

"Shotgun!" I shouted racing to passenger side hoping a car wouldn't hit me.

As everyone's seat buckles clicked, the hot driver merged with traffic heading to Tu Lan.

• • • • •

Halfway to our destination, my curiosity got the better of me.

"Do you have a girlfriend?" I asked.

"Not currently," the Uber driver replied.

That answered my "what team is he batting for" question. Eve suggested we take picture of us in the car, which I happily encouraged. Whipping out my phone, I waited for everyone to fix their hair and pose before counting down from three. Taking a few, Lucy suggested we include the

---

[50] I'm telling you, these girls are hotel pirates.

[51] If you haven't figured it out, San Francisco guys are known to wear only button shirts. It's the only thing in their closet.

driver. He smiled and we waited for a stoplight. I held up the phone and counted to three again.

"Are you going to school for anything?" I asked, posing another question to our handsome driver.

"I want to become a pilot," he said with a smile.

"So, if we need a flight somewhere do we request you on Uber?" I said, flirting.

He giggled at my minor joke. I placed my hand on his arm telling him I was kidding. The young driver didn't mind my hand touching him.

"All right, here you guys go," the driver said a bit loudly.

An echoed "thank you" filled the car as everyone vacated. Shutting my door, I waved him off and then turned around to see that the restaurant that Sawyer's friend had suggested—and supposedly reserved— was nothing but a filthy hole in the wall that could only fit five people at a time; any more and it would exceed the maximum limit.[52]

Sawyer is now on my shit list.

There he was bragging about how his friend knew the city and could get us in to a really nice restaurant anywhere. Not only were his true colors showing, but his words had become hollow. Not only does he look bad, but he roped me in. Eve, Kitty, Taron, and Lucy regarded at me with such disappointment. Seconds later, Sawyer, got out of his Uber and greeted us with smile.

"Tu Lan is a dump!" I loudly told Sawyer.

The smile fell from Sawyer's face when he looked inside the hole in the wall. He shook his head in dissatisfac-

---

[52] And already 3 of 5 those spots were already taken by the cooks—so really only two.

tion as he muttered his friend's name under his breath. No apology, no coming forward, or owning his mistake...nothing. Telling Taron to look up any nearby restaurants, we found one that was close by—Urban Tavern. Calling the number listed, we reserved a table.[53]

• • • • •

Urban Tavern looked and felt more like the vibe the five of us originally expected: low lighting with a hint of mellow. At the front desk, a woman in her late thirties waited for the name of our reservation. After providing my name, she apologized for the inconvenience before telling us that the table promised wasn't ready and that the party was still paying for their check. She offered us the waiting area that was collection of tan couches located near the bar to the left of us. Nodding, all six of us headed to the bar first before moving to the waiting area.

An unusually quiet Sawyer sat right in front of me. He purposely ignored everyone and myself and played on his phone. I figured I should send him a text and get the ball rolling on the conversation we're going to have sooner or later. So, I did: I'm really upset.

I watched him open and read the text. Irritation crossed his face, and then he took sip of his white wine. He clicked his phone off and dropped it into his lap.

And now I had to wait.

---

[53] This is what happens when I let others take the reins.

• • • • •

Twenty minutes.

That's how long it took for us to be seated at a table. What happened to the people paying their check? Did they suddenly forget how to do the math for leaving a proper tip? Were they trying to figure out how to dine and dash? Regardless, the restaurant showered us with appetizers as an apology for keeping us waiting longer.

Sitting at my head of the table, I noticed Eve and Sawyer talking in the middle of the ramp that lead to the dining area. His back was to me and Eve faced my direction. Watching the interaction, Eve was on the defensive. When the conversation abruptly ended, Sawyer approached and placed his glass and jacket down at the table next to me before walking into the hallway leading to the restrooms. Eve sat herself at the table next to Kitty and Taron.

"What the fuck happened?" I asked.

"He doesn't understand why you would be upset with him and thinks that you need to separate business from pleasure. I then told him that the reason you didn't show up to his camping trip was because I was going through something and by the end of the day you were going to choose me before him." Eve explained.

Sawyer returned from the restroom, aggressively sitting down on my left. Everyone became uncomfortably quiet and looked over their menus. This is not how I wanted the trip to go. Sawyer had caused more issues than anyone else I've invited in the past—probably the last time I ever do something like this. The outcome of our trip so far would have been way different.

Later, after we shared toasts and everyone enjoyed what they ordered, it was time to have that uncomfortable conversation with the man I invited.

"We need to talk," I whispered.

"All right," Sawyer said as he got up from his seat.

"We can talk right here."

"Nope!" he said, heading to the restroom hallway.

Let the drama begin.

I followed Sawyer into the hallway. He turned to face me with a wide-eyed angry expression, like he was on the verge of insanity.

"I'm uncomfortable. Sharing a hotel room with five other people is not a good idea. I'm trying to make nice with your friends and it's simply too much. I'm five years older than you.[54] I know what I want and I'm not going to change. You didn't show up to my camping birthday party

---

[54] You may be 35, but subtract thirty from your age and you get his real age.

trip.[55] We barely know each other," Sawyer angrily said.

Reading his body language—crossed arms and tapping his foot repeatedly—he was acting more like a spoiled five-year-old than a calm thirty-five-year-old. No matter what I what I said, he was going to condemn me for it.

"I hate Reno! I also took that into consideration," he added.

"You've made that quite clear," I calmly said.

If Sawyer had already taken in account that we lived in different cities and wasn't going to take this seriously, then him being here wasn't to see if we were compatible for more than just a friendship. It was clear this was just an excuse for him leave his crap in the hotel while he ventured without me or my friends. Sawyer was using me.[56]

I spoke next, "I'm going to give you an hour to head back to the hotel, pack up your stuff, and stay with the friends you brag about who have a room for you anytime you come to San Francisco. It's apparent you prefer to stay with them, even if they are getting a divorce."

"Fine," Sawyer huffed.

Just like that, he turned away from me and went back to our table. Picking up his bag, he told my friends to have a good night before walking off. Stunned eyes regarded me, and the looks on their faces telepathically asked what happened.

"I excused him and his *legerdemain*," I promptly told them, raising my hands a little.

---

[55] Is he really stuck on that? The trip was three months ago and really needs to let that go. I apologized and that's why I invited him.

[56] Strike three.

"Is he not going to pay for his meal?" Kitty asked.

I sighed and whipped out my debit card. "No, I'm going to."

"That's bullshit!" an angry Eve loudly said.

"You've spent too much time and money on that asshole," Lucy said, staring at my debit card, "We'll help you."

I couldn't believe it. All my friends were pitching in to pay his bill—mind you, Sawyer ordered a few things off the menu that weren't cheap. I felt very grateful to be surrounded by such amazing people who didn't have pay for the mess I invited.

• • • • •

Back at the Monarch Hotel, standing in the hallway just outside our hotel room, I told everyone to wait while I checked to see if he was still in the room collecting his things. It had been over an hour and he should have cleared out by now. Swiping the card, I counted to three, hoping one of two things: one, that Sawyer wasn't in the room, and two, that Sawyer didn't destroy everyone's stuff, including the room.

Opening the door, I peaked my head in to find that he wasn't there. Stepping in further to check the room out, I saw nothing out of place except for any empty area in the closet where his stuff was.

Nothing was damaged.

The only thing he left behind was a note written on the mirror in white eyeliner: "Have fun in San Francisco!"

"What the hell is this RuPaul nonsense?" I asked no one

in particular, irritated.

Eve walked over to the mirror with a damp wash cloth, and said, "Sashay away" as she wiped it clean.

"That better have not been written with any of my eye-liners!" Lucy shouted.

10

From Folsom With Love...
Lots and Lots of Love

— SAN FRANCISCO PART III —

Where the hell was this Uber driver taking us? On the flyer, it said from 8th and 13th, yet, I'm watching the 18th, 19th, and 20th street signs fly by.

"This is good...Thank you," I told him, feeling frustrated.

The Uber driver nodded and pulled over.[57] Kitty and her boyfriend made their way to sidewalk, just as confused as I was. *Sidenote*: Eve couldn't make it—she was heading to Las Vegas—while Lucy had other engagements she planned

---

[57] He is so not getting a tip.

before this.

So, it was just the three of us—and we were all BDSM virgins.

Taking a glance at my surroundings, a guy in nothing but a leather jockstrap walked by us, heading north on Folsom St.

"Look! A guy in all leather...where ever he's going, that's where we need to be," I said, directing my fellow virgins.[58]

Somewhere between 17th and 15th, the man walked joined up with a group of men in leather apparel that appeared out of nowhere. The gaggle of gays each had their own flare to them. Some of them wore symmetrical or asymmetrical (one shoulder) chest harnesses with and leather shorts or leather under-somethings. I don't know how they exerted such confidence walking down the street half-naked. They all acted as though it was just a normal Sunday in San Fran. Even the kids at a nearby park didn't gawk in shock at the sight.[59]

My nerves started acting up after hearing distant echoes of music. Straight ahead, on the other side of a frantically busy cross street, was the start of 13th. I could see people gathering around the entrance and paying their dues of $10. The reasonably long line only had people in leather, but there were individuals in vibrant boas, mascot gear (furries), and people in everyday clothes.

In other words, it was an adult version of Sesame

---

[58] Totally had a Miranda moment and didn't even realize it.

[59] I still think they should be covered up until they get to the fair. But that's the problem with gays of this generation: they just don't care.

Street.[60] I can totally picture Big Bird in a harness, shades, and hat smoking a cigar while holding a chained leash attached to Snuffy trailing behind.

The three of us paid our dues and went through the checkpoint. I excused myself and entered a popping bar to change into my Folsom attire. Inside, the restroom was just off to the right. On the door was a sign that indicated that only paying customer could use it. Checking to see if anybody was watching—they weren't—I slipped in and locked the door.

Turning on the light, I saw the restroom was completely red, including the lightbulb. It reminded me of the photography developing room I used during my college years.

Opening my backpack, I removed my black combat boots and the black glittered bunny mask and replaced them with my jeans, tank top, and Toms. In that moment, all I wore was my semi-sheer yellow and blue EROS briefs that not only complimented my booty, but my package as well. In seconds, I was ready. Looking at my reflection in the crusty scratched mirror—the kind you only see in movies—I took in a deep breath. This was something I said I would never do.

I needed a pep talk with myself.

---

[60] The word of the day is DOMINATE.

"Allister, you can do this. Remember the reason you wanted to do this: you no longer want to be vanilla. You are going to walk out of this restroom with your head held high and own it. Now, repeat it: you're not vanilla. I'm not vanilla...I'm not vanilla...I'M NOT VANILLA!"

I didn't mean to raise my voice.

Putting on the glittered bunny mask, I unlocked and opened the door and saw a man leaning against the bar, facing me with raised eyebrows. If I was going to keep these pep talks to myself, it's best not to get overly excited. He probably thought I was a wack job.

Smiling back, I headed out the bar.

Kitty and Taron were waiting around the corner staring—not gazing—and intensely people watching.

"Viola! What do you guys think?" I shouted.

"You look amazing!"Kitty said with a big smiled.

"Adorable!" Taron added.

That was the exact confidence boost I needed.

Handing my backpack to Taron, we headed out into the leather wilderness of Folsom Street.

• • • • •

People gathered around a booth that displayed a blindfolded woman in pink bondage who was completely suspended, her hands tied behind her. She spun slowly, giving everybody a full view of what her dominant was about to do.

A man in a mask came out from a tent-like structure holding a paddle and a silver object. Making himself known, he grazed the paddle against her leg. She shook lightly, but welcomed him with a moan letting him know she was at his whim. Her dominant completely ignored the crowd by not making any eye contact with us.

"Do you know your safe word?"[61] he asked.

"I do, sir," she confirmed.

Getting down on his knees, he spun his sub until he faced her vagina. Licking the silver object, he slowly penetrated her. Flinging her head back, she gasp with utter pleasure. Wide-eyed at this point, I wondered how could they be so comfortable performing sexual acts in public. Hell, it took a lot of courage for me to even step out of the bar restroom in this getup.

Mr. Dom, now standing, gently tapping the paddle against her ass, causing her to giggle until he gave it a firm smack. His body language didn't reveal how much this pleasured him, but his eyes said plenty. Ms. Sub bit her bottom lip, trying to contain her moan. Watching this was like tuning into an episode of National Geographic.

In a British accent: "Watch as we see the sub giving herself completely to the dominant as he performs the mating ritual."

Most of the people around me chuckled at my minor

---

[61] Yes, supercalifragilisticexpialidocious.

joke.

Mr. Dom continued to give her little pats followed by a firm smack. Kitty suggested we move on as it no longer piqued her interested. We pulled away from the crowd and merged with clusterfuck of people heading deeper into the fair. A patron chilling on the sidewalk noticed my bunny mask and screamed out "DANGEROUS WOMAN," pointed at me, and nodded in satisfaction. Slightly embarrassed, I winked in acknowledgement.

The three of us found ourselves at a four-way stop intersection that allowed us to space out a bit. Taron felt parched and noticed someone selling pouches of water for $2. I decided to whip out my phone from my backpack and take pictures.

"Woof!" a man in his mid-forties said loudly.

"Thank you," I politely said.

He and a couple of his friends looked me up and down, like a lion getting ready to pounce on a gazelle.

After I was done taking some pictures one of the men in the group spoke up.

"Where are you going to put that?" the *woofed* man asked.

"In my hand," I rudely responded.

"Feisty. I like feisty."

"You couldn't handle this," I replied in a sassy tone.

"Only one way to find out," he said, closing the distance between us.

"All right, time to go!"

Collecting my straight friends, we headed back into the highway of people and disappeared into the crowd. Usually guys of that caliber back down after I exert some sassiness. I found out that didn't work well on Folsom Street.

And I could see why.

Another booth, surrounded by an assortment of on-lookers, showcased two men in masks having full on, bare-back, deeply penetrative, panting, anal sex.

This is what many people warned me about, yet, I wasn't taken aback by the sight of it. However, I felt a bit uncomfortable. You know that feeling you get when you watch a sex scene in a movie with your parents? It was like that but with my straight friends. Kitty's eyes were glued to the dick-to-ass contact while Taron looked at the reactions of the audience.

I felt a tap on my shoulder, followed by an "excuse me." Turning around, a man with a camera asked if he could take my picture. Nodding, I posed. The photographer thanked me before heading elsewhere, looking for his next model(s).

Poor Kitty. I wasn't sure if she was intrigued or stunned by the sex show.

"Anybody up for some ice cream?" I asked.

"Meeeee!" Kitty shouted.

I knew sweets would pull her out of the sex-booty-trance she was caught up in. To be honest, it's been a long time since I've had any form of good sex, besides porn...so I better savor this moment.

A few minutes later, we cut through the various groups of people, the sounds of an ice cream truck guiding us. The line was short, so we got our frozen treats quickly.

"Ariana!" a disembodied voice moaned.

As a I turned around, a young twenty-something guy

immediately reached out and pinched my nipple. Kitty, who was standing next to me, couldn't believe what just happened.

"Guys just do that?" she asked.

"Normally, no. But I think once we entered, we sorta lost the right to consent," I said, licking my ice cream.

"Do you need me to beat anyone up?" Taron offered.

"No, no. That won't be necessary. We're here for a day. Let's just let what ever happens, happen," I said.

"Your bodyguard is ready!"

Just like the nipple pincher, a man holding a camera came out of nowhere and asked for a photo.

"Second one today." I loudly announced.

Posing for the photo, other gawking leather patrons around us snapped photos with their phones.[62]

After getting the photographer's information as to where I could find the photo, the weather quickly changed from sunshine to overcast, and the air grew colder. It was time to call it quits on Folsom Street. Heading back to where we started, the crowd somehow thickened. I spotted a familiar face though the sea of people.

---

[62] Queerty, DNA, Attitude, & Out Magazine here I come!

Scott McGlothen, a.k.a, Bareinkslinger.

A blogger who bares it all—well, that's what his insta-gram says. He and I have chatted, slowly becoming Internet buddies checking in with one another to see how our travels are doing.

"Fancy meeting you here!" I said, coming up behind him.

"Hey?" he said with a bit of confusion.

Taking off the mask, the lightbulb turned on in Scott's head.

"I didn't recognized you with that mask on."

"You're not the only one, sir," I said.

It was a quick hello and goodbye because others who wanted his attention bombarded him. Well, when you blog about your life events completely nude—with photos—those who are thirsty will try as they might to somehow play naked twister with you. Hell, there's one in the middle of the whole Folsom event, too!

It's a sign!

In the back of my mind—during this whole escapade—was Sawyer. I was on the lookout for him, intent on dodging him at all costs. Even though he left, he was still in the city and at the booth he does PR work for. After what he pulled, he deserves a punch in the face. Ugh! Is that how he treats people? Wouldn't put it past him, as he talks negatively about his clients.

Dismissing him from dinner was the best decision I've ever made.

"WOOF!" a man inches away from me whispers, scar-ing me half to death.

"Oh my god!" I shouted, cringing.

"Don't worry, I'm not gonna touch you...unless you want me to."

"I'm afraid not, as I'm a *look but don't touch* kinda guy," I said, letting him down.

"Shame," the beefy man said with a smile.

Shrugging my shoulders, the man walked on, probably looking for someone else to *woof.* Now, we were off to find the nearest exit from this leather BDSM-crazed world so I could put my clothes back on.

~~6. FOLSOM STREET FAIR~~

11

An Invite Or Discouragement

— SAN FRANCISCO PART IV —

Squeaky.........Squeaky.........Squeaky.......Squeaky......Squeaky...
Squeaky...Squeaky...Squeaky...Squeaky, Squeaky, Squeaky,
Squeaky, Squeaky, Squeaky, Squeaky, Squeaky.

"You have to be fucking kidding me!" I said to myself
while staring at the ceiling.

Was room 610 really having sex at five in the morning?
They had awoken me two hours before my alarm was
scheduled to go off. So, instead of waking up to an annoying alarm, the sounds of a squeaking old bed in desperate
need of WD-40 and moans from two gay men jump-started
my last day in San Francisco.

"Yeah, daddy...give it to me," a muffled voice said.

"Karma, are you mocking me?" I said.

Should I just go upstairs, bust down the door, and announce, "Player three has entered the game?"

Getting up from bed, it was a sign I overstayed my welcome in the city, or maybe San Francisco was telling me I need to back my sexual drive.

To knock on the door or not to knock on the door? That was the question...

October 23, 2018

Dear August,

Folsom was interesting, to say the least, and I'll probably never go back. It's just not my scene, and with the amount of "woofs", gay men reaching out to either pinch my nipple or touch my booty, and being called Ariana Grande—due to the bunny ears—I'll savor the memory in the years to come. No need for an annual repeat. Drinking champagne at Tiffany & Co had to be the best part of trip.

Just got back from my trip to San Jose. The book signing went very well and I met some rather interesting individuals. One woman—after explaining what my book was about—starting crying. Under the blubbering, she was beginning to be bitter herself from her recent divorce. Wasn't exactly sure what she looking for, but the crying woman bought a copy and disappeared into the book store.

Saturday night, I made the announcement that I wanted to lock lips with someone. Eve, who was already drunk from many glasses of champagne, said that my wing-woman was present and ready to make that happen. By the time we got to Splash, I had changed my mind. It had become too intimidating to carry out the plan. Not Eve.

She had managed to find me a guy—who I already spotted and caught, many times, staring at me—and introduced us. In a matter of minutes I found out he was 23, deals with computers, and just moved to San Jose. We danced and made out. My dumb ass invited him back to the hotel.

I was looking to just cuddle. My return home flight the next day (Sunday) boarded at 6:50 in the morning. The 23-year-old said that was fine and we ended the night cuddling until, I got up and asked if he wanted to take a shower. Then my dumb ass caved into the pleasure and I had sex with him. Cannot believe I did that. Now, I feel completely hollow. The 23-year-old may feel fine, but this 29-year-old feels like whore.

Always,

Allister

To: *Allister_at_home*
From: *August_at_home*
Subject: RE: *AM I A DUMBASS OR A WHORE OR BOTH?*

October 23, 2018

Hi Allister,
You've not done anything I haven't done before... probably

dozens of times. Men are naturally hedonistic. Restraint isn't really in of our bag of tricks.

If your experience is anything like mine: in my teens and 20s I loved bed-hopping. I moved to a bigger city and continued to love it. Unknowingly a void formed—I had no real close male friendships and no relationship outside of a few dates, but I could easily get laid. I tried filling it with other things when sex was no longer enough on its own. All that came to a head, and a couple of years later (when I turned 40) I realized I no longer liked the bar hopping and bed hopping scene.

I've thought my rocky relationships might be from hopping into bed too quickly—men (myself included) like the chase, the feeling of going after sex; it's better than sex itself. And once that's over, sometimes there's not much left because there wasn't much developed.

As for Eve: This is stereotypical and bad—but I've never had a high number of hetero—female friends outside of work . Maybe a few. When I was drinking and bar hopping, all the straight women I'd see at the bar were acting like total twats, and I just could not deal. Eve sounds like the type.

You're not a whore. We keep doing the things we do until we are really ready for change. Until that point, we revert to what we know best.

You'll feel better after a couple of days.

Take care,

August

To: *August_at_home*
From: *Allister_at_home*
Subject: RE: RE: *AM I A DUMBASS OR A WHORE OR BOTH?*

October 23, 2018

Dear August,

I'm trying to distance myself from sex. Like you said before, it feels hollow and unsatisfying. A simple make-out session would have sufficed. I'm at the point in my life that I no longer crave sex like one craves a pint of Ben and Jerry's or hot Cheetos—still not sure why people crave that, nonetheless, it's craved.

Regression is something I'm wanting in my life. So, the way it's adding up in my head is...Me + No Sex = No acting on bad habits. Logical, right? I want to focus more on ending my twenties and welcoming my thirties without any pot holes in the road. Bumps have been endured along the way, but nothing I can't handle. Sex, however, causes me to experience huge, confusing episodes. The human touch is such a powerful sense for me. Maybe, and I say maybe boldly, celibacy is the way to go, or do you feel it's another dumb-ass move I'd be doing?

Always,

Allister

To: *Allister_at_home*
From: *August_at_home*
Subject: RE: RE: RE: *AM I A DUMBASS OR A WHORE OR BOTH?*

October 23, 2018

Hi Allister,

I did a vow of celibacy in January (law of chastity), and you do feel good—really good—especially if you cease porn use (if you're into that, I was) and no jerking off. It feels like a let down though, if you cave.

Take care,

August

12

Just Watch My Goddamn Bag!

And whose idea was it to plan an event at 8:30pm during winter?

Somebody who obviously loves the fucking cold!

Every year, the university (that remain nameless) hosts a very unique 5k called the Undie Run.[63] When they 5k, they really mean a one-mile circle because god forbid these Generation Z's run more than that. It's for a good cause though; you donate the clothes on your back to those who need it.

After finding a parking spot on the street a couple

---

[63] FYI, this story happened before getting pneumonia. So, I apologize for the lack of toned body and beard.

blocks away from campus, Mike and I walked through the residential area to avoid paying for parking. I believe that parking laws should be the same for campus. Free parking after 6 p.m. for all!

Mike and I were stopped by a drunk twenty-something kid and his pals who were in their backyard tossing the pig skin around while passing the joint around. The kid was about to throw the ball to one of us, and Mike seemed unsure he should do that.

"What are you guys up to tonight?" Mr. Drunk asked.

"We're heading to campus for the annual Undie Run," I said, shivering.

"What? What time does that start?" he said, slurring.

"Everybody is gathering in front of Crowley now, won't be running until nine," Mike replied.

"Let's see your undies, men!"

Bicurious? I think so.

Mike and I pulled our shorts down to reveal our square cut trunks. Mike wore a pair of black Calvin Klein briefs while I wore a powder blue 2xist pair.[64]

"Hot! I'm a bit fat, do think people would care?" he asked,

"Don't think that matters," Mike said.

"I don't know if I want to go, but have a good night though," Mr. Drunk said before returning to throw the ball around...terribly.

"That guy was pretty fucked up!" Mike said.

"How is he still functioning?" I said.

---

[64] Bought those specifically for this! And might I say...bootytastic.

Crossing the street, Mike and I saw a large group of students in nothing but trunks, panties, and thongs bouncing and dancing to the music provided by the school.

All the students had perfect bodies. Abs...pecs...even Michelle Obama arms! Memories of past San Francisco Pride flashed before my eyes. Not again! I'm a 2 in a sea of 10's.

"Is it too late to turn back now Mike?" I asked, wide-eyed.

"Nope! We're here and you're stripping!" he said.

Nodding, the only problem I had was my bag. Where was I going to stash it so that it wouldn't be stolen? I wanted to know it would be safe when I would return from my undie escapade because it held my keys, debit card, ID, and extra clothes.

Looking around, I saw a line people signing the waiver. I wasn't sure what we had to signing off on. Was I signing off that I was one garment away from being naked, and if someone were to pants me, the university would not held responsible for my nakedness or me losing any shred of dignity?

After signing off and receiving a yellow wrist band, I was still hunting for a place to stash my bag. Beyond the sea of underwear people, I spied a lonely girl sitting at a table collecting clothes from people. I approached, with Mike trailing behind me, and asked if she could watch my bag while we did the run.

"Well, you could leave it but I won't be responsible for it," she said with an attitude.

"I see. Remember what you just said. Karma's a bitch

and it comes back three times worse. But have a good night. Hopefully you don't drop out and end up selling yourself to make rent unlike someone I know," I said locking eyes with the girl.

Finding another table with a lonely girl, drinking her white-girl pumpkin latte, I asked the same question.

"I wish I could..."

"But you're not responsible if it gets stolen. Got the same response that nasty girl over there. Thanks."

Walking away, an idea came to me...

"Do you think I should leave it over by the DJ area?[65] They're going to be here all night," I asked Mike.

"I don't see why not," he answered.

Heading over to the canopy that blasted awful techno and dubstep, there was a girl working the booth that we both knew. Looking back at Mike, he also noticed the familiar girl screaming out her name.

"Beth!"

"Mike, Allister!" she screamed back.

"How are you?" Mike asked.

"I'm good, but freezing my big ass off. What are you guys doing here?"

"It's an item on my bucket list," I said.

"Good for you!"

"I have a favor to ask of you."

"Sure," she said.

"Could you watch my bag while Mike and I do the run?"

---

[65] Sorry to break away from the story, but my editor couldn't help but comment on this by saying "why didn't you just wear it?" Bitch, I don't know! Love you, though.

She hesitated, "You can but..."

Cutting her off, I said, "You're not responsible if it gets taken."

"Right."

"It's fine, I'll leave it. And if it gets taken, then it does," setting the bag next to her.

What is it with people nowadays? All I asked was for someone to just keep an eye on it, not strap it to their body and guard it with their life![66] Grabbing the important items out of the bag, I stripped down to my undies and left the bag with DJ Beth. The air was so brisk that my body started to shrivel up and shiver to keep warm. Mike and I stretched for bit so we wouldn't end up hurting the next day.

"I have to pee!" Mike announced.

"We have ten minutes before everybody starts running," I said.

"Either I go now or I'll piss my undies," he said, not giving me a choice.

"Potty stop it is."

Quickly heading inside the Crowley building, Mike entered the bathroom while I waited in the common area. Amusingly, the front desk person checked me out.

"This is probably not the most awkward thing you've seen on campus," I said, breaking the silence.

"Nope," the front desk girl replied.

"Normally, I don't do anything like this."

"Hey, no worries. You don't have to explain why you're standing here in your underwear."

---

[66] Like it's hard!

Taking that as a hint to shut up, Mike finally came out of the bathroom, empty and ready to go.

Back outside in the brisk cold night air, the announcer gathered the participants to the starting line. We were so close to one another that we could smell the overly fragranced bodies of those around us. The man behind the microphone started the countdown from ten as others joined in. At the word "go," the crowd slowly moved forward and dispersed into the road.

Many of the girls clung to one another for warmth while jogging. Maybe wearing a thong was a bad idea, ladies. Some of the students took this 5k too seriously and were jumping off of small ledges, carrying ladies, and even screaming at the top of their lungs chanting, "We can do this." I was trying to make it all the way through without passing out.

Your chanting does nothing! Mike, on the other hand, acted like this was nothing, like he could do this all-day long.

Halfway through, I saw other people running in the opposite direction. Thank god! I thought this was going to go on forever.

"Lookout!" I heard someone say.

Facing forward, a couple of fit guys were running toward us. They nearly caused head on collisions with runners, including myself. The officials on the sideline who held flashlights to guide our way yelled at the runners to get on the left side and stay there.[67]

Making a U-turn around a large tree, a few people behind me made a sounds like someone got hurt. Turning around—running backward—I saw one of the undie runners had flipped and fallen on his back. Covered in scrapes and bruises, he just laid there. He had attempted to run through an area marked off with rope. Did he purposefully run toward the marked area thinking he could jump over it and try to impress some of the ladies around him or did he truly not see the rope?

Oh well, he'll learn.

Facing forward with Mike still trailing behind me, we weaved through the crowd, many of whom had stopped to walk and catch their breath.

"Slow down, you're too fucking fast, Allister!" Mike exclaimed.

"Sorry, I'm just focused and when I run, I run," I said.

The sound of music became louder as we approached the finish line, which in this case was the same as the starting line. Just as Mike came up beside me, a guy just ahead us started to countdown from five. Then he and the group with him started to sing a Christmas song.

What the hell was this?

Leaning over to Mike I said, "Watch this." Mike wasn't sure what I was going to do, but he waited to see the rebuttal. The group finished their Christmas carol, and I jumped

---

[67] But if they had a gorgeous smile and abs they could run into me.

in...

"This is Halloween, this is Halloween, fa la la!"

Those who had sung the Christmas carol briefly glanced back and regarded me with incredible disapproval. I shrugged my shoulders with a smile. The next time you decide to pull a stunt like that, make sure you're not in the presences of one who values Halloween like one who goes to church every Sunday.

Mike and I ditched the inconsiderate group and finished out the run. I collapsed on the cold grass and my body gave out. I had pushed myself beyond my limits and maybe shouldn't have. I didn't want to stop at any point. After all, it's not a run if you stop and walk.

"Everything okay?" Mike asked.

"Give...me...a...second," I said, trying to catch my breath.

Mike laughed and walked over to the DJ booth to grab my bag. It probably wasn't a good idea to lay on the grass,[68] but at that moment I didn't care.

"Here you go," Mike said, handing me my bag.

Getting up from the wet grass, I gradually got dressed. Mike, on the other hand, had donated the sweatpants he was wearing and didn't bring an extra pair. So, there we were, walking through the residential area back to my parked car with him in his underwear and a beanie. What would people think when they saw us walking? $100 dollars to the person with the best caption!

Making it home after dropping Mike back at his place, I pulled out my Glitter List and crossed off the item with a

---

[68] Some nasty acts could have taken place...urinating, sex, you just don't know.

gold colored Sharpie:

2. ~~UNDIE RUN~~

13

French Lesson

Days of week

Lundi—Monday
Mardi—Tuesday
Mercredi—Wednesday
Jeudi—Thursday

Vendredi—Friday
Samedi—Saturday
Dimanche—Sunday

Months

Janvier—January
Février—February
Mars—March
Avril—April
Mai—May
Juin—June

Juillet—July
Août—August
Septembre—September
Octobre—October
Novembre—November

Dècembre—December

Seasons

The Spring—Le printemps   The Winter—L'hiver

The Fall—L'automne   The Summer—L'ètè

Now that I have the months and seasons down, time for numbers...it never ends.

242

From the Desk of Allister B. Dean

· ·

Cosmopolitan Magazine

For years, I've purchased and/or subscribed to your magazine as it has always brought me a sense of enjoyment. Plus, it has given me excellent sex tips for when the moment falls into my lap. Little do any of the men I've been with know I've used some of those tips on them to see if they actually worked... guinea pigs, if you will.

I have to say, each issue this year has been better than the previous month. Upon receiving your December 2018 issue—I came across the article, *"Celebrate Your Breakup,"* and noticed that it was all too familiar. In said article, the writer suggested that one shouldn't wallow in the split, but rather celebrate one's new freedom with friends. In my last memoir, *Brutally Bitter* (that was released over two years ago,) I wrote about a *Singleversary,* an event to toast/celebrate the accomplishment of not being in a relationship for over a year.

Has someone from your publication decided it was okay to bounce from that idea, making it their own after reading my book? Imitation is the most sincere form of flattery, but come on...let's be original here! You're a publication that's supposed to come up with fresh ideas and create trends, not borrow from someone else.

This is utter bullshit and you know it!

UTTER BULLSHIT!

I'm a bit weary of what's to come in the January 2019 issue or any future ones at that, as I'm afraid to wander through your pages and find another of my ideas buried in it. This minor infraction won't detract me from my readership with you.

Always,

Allister

To: *Eve_at_home, Kitty_at_home, Lucy_at_home*
From: *Allister_at_home*
Subject: *Are You Supposed To Be A Girl?*

November 1, 2018

Loves,

What the hell is wrong with trick-or-treaters nowadays!?

Everything was going rather smoothly. As its my first year passing out candy, I decided to get into the spirit of things by wearing my black-glittered bunny mask. A girl of merely 11 comes to my door and upon seeing the mask, asks loudly in front of two other kids, *"Are you trying to be a girl?"*

What the fuck? How dare she throw shady insults my way.

The young girl was dressed in what appeared to be a wedding gown, covered in large amounts blood which also dribbled out of her mouth. She was a dead bride.

Hopefully, Aunt Flow is slowly killing her from the inside.

"Nope, just a fabulous bunny," I told her.

I was ready for this little bitch, but I held back the insult that formed at the tip of my tongue. "I can see why your husband killed you." I wouldn't have cared if her parents heard me.

Instead, I gave her some candy and kept my mouth shut. These kids are getting bolder each year. I blame the parents for not taking contraception more seriously.

Always,

Allister

———————————————————————————

14

When In Doubt, Choose Option C

A week and half prior to the big day, I reached out to our current mayor—via twitter—who was running for another term. I wanted to see what she was planning for my hometown. She was one of the few who wasn't running smear campaigns against her opposition.

ALLISTER DEAN @allister_in_wonderland · 10/27/18

@Mayor.S I'm voting for the first time this year and everyone who I've come into contact with has said to vote for you...could you explain your plans for Reno? Haven't seen any campaigns online or on television telling me what your future plans are.

MAYOR.S @mayorschieve · 10/27/18

@allister_dean WOOHOO! Congratulations on becoming a first time Reno voter! You can visit my campaign at mayor.s.com You can also email me your phone number. I am happy to call you back! #LetsVote

---

I never heard from her after sending my email with my phone number attached.[69]

November 6th... election day.

A day where people cast their vote on who they feel would be a good fit to serve the state/city in which they currently reside. In other words, a group of people who secretly hate it each other but smile to keep the peace. Funny though, people are much braver on Facebook than in person.

Here I was, standing in a ridiculously small gymnasium at a middle school in a long voluted line leading out the door. This is what I get for living in a neighborhood/community that's twenty minutes outside the city.

Just as you walk in, a sign indicated the limit of people allowed in this room, which was 55. The fire marshal would've had a field day if he knew these voluntolds[70] had exceeded the code. Even the parking situation was chaotic. Anticipating this, I had walked because my house was only five minutes from the middle school. Plus, it was a beautiful day with not a cloud in sight.

Hiding behind my huge sunglasses, I began to check

---

[69] Makes you wonder about the people who want to represent you in office.

[70] Voluntold: (n) a person who volunteers for sheer pleasure, but is giving an unpleasant task.

out the other voters around me. To my surprise, coming to the polls dressed like you just rolled out of bed seemed to be the trending look everybody strove for. And here I was, wearing my boots, jeans, and a button shirt.[71] But that all changed when a man with severely bleached tan wingtip shoes walked in. Apparently, he decided it was a good idea to wear dark denim with a dark collared shirt. If you were to see this guy, his tan shoes would be all that screamed at you.

I gave him an A for effort, though.

Weaving through the line, one short step at a time, a couple behind me had nothing good to say about the location.

"Offering coffee at this thing would have been nice," one of them said in a low voice.

This isn't a hotel, bud! Should have brought your own, I did! Mine even has something a little extra, if you catch my drift.[72] The couple continued on with their negative, condescending conversation until a familiar face interrupted them.

"Hi guys, how are the two of you?" a woman asked, approaching the couple.

"We're doing good, and you, Vivian?" they asked.

"Old and fat."

"Well, if the girdle doesn't fit," I said to myself, silently participating in their conversation.

"Can you believe how many people are here? At least provide some damn coffee for those of us waiting in line!"

---

[71] Still feeling the San Francisco vibes back in September.
[72] 70/30 ratio. 30% is the coffee.

an upset Vivian announced.

"We just got done saying that."

This is why they're friends. Complainers group with other complainers to form a super-complainer band, also known as protesters. But, just as quickly as she showed up, she left. Maybe she guessed I was tuning into their bitchfest.

Who knows?

People watching yet again, a scruffy man walked through the door and made my day. It looked as though he just came from working a ranch with his shit kickers, boot-cut Levi's, and plaid shirt. What caught my attention was the shinny, metallic, fur-lined vest disco-balling in the sun-light. Either he thinks he's a space cowboy listening to too much Kid Rock or he doesn't give a fabulous fuck about what he wears. Regardless, it made my fucking day and made it worth standing in this line!

• • • • •

Reaching the front table, I saw three up-there-in-age voluntolds signing people in. One of them, a gentleman, signaled for me to step forward.

"Last name and zip code please," he said.

"Dean, 89508."

"Allister?"

"Yep, that's me," I gleefully said.

His facial expression was constantly emotionless during our entire interaction. He pointed to the little screen in front of me and told me to sign while he printed out a small label and placed it in a book much like voters before me.

Next, he handed me a plastic-sized debit card that had a chip on the bottom with voter shit on the top.

"Next!" he yelled.

Scooting off to the left, I looked to see if any of the booths were available. All were occupied, but didn't have to wait very long. Heading to the end, each person I passed had look of utter confusion or regret about the decision they made. I inserted the voter debit card and watched the screen come alive as it made loud beeping noises.

Even though it wasn't a test of any sort, my test anxiety kicked in. The first set of questions appeared on the screen: State Senate, Representative of Congress District 2, Secretary of State, and the list went on. I marked off the people I had researched on and felt would be a good fit—those smear campaigns are simply a joke. Most of the sections only had one person in it, so the choice was made for me. I was doing pretty good, and I felt very political.

Yay me! Maybe, I should do this more often, but with cocktails.

The last section was my for Governor and the list was long—but there weren't many candidates from the last election:

- Best
- Bundy

- Laxalt
- Lord
- Sisolak

I totally forgot Governor!

I knew very little or nothing at all about the choices, so I attempted the process of elimination approach. Best, or so he thinks...nope. Bundy, reminds me of Paul Bundy...nope. Laxalt, sounds like a salt laxative... nope. Lord, we already have one and her music is *aight*[73]... nope Sisolak; I don't know your last name...nope. That got me nowhere.

Eenie, meenie, miney, mo. Catch a tiger by his toe. If he hollers, let him go. Eenie, meenie, miney, mo. Nope, don't like that person.

Fuck it. When in doubt, choose option C.

Pressing done, the machine recorded my vote and told me to remove the card from the machine. Walking back to the table, I greeted the emotionless voluntold again and handed him my voter debit card. He pointed, yet again, to a woman by the door handing out stickers that said, "I voted." Nodding, I grabbed my 2x2 round sticker and headed home for a nap. Performing my civic duty took a lot out of me!

~~5. VOTE~~

---

[73] Not a spelling error, think slang.

To: *Allister_at_home*
From: *August_at_home*
Subject: *Happy Thanksgiving!*

November 22, 2018

Hi Allister,

Happy Thanksgiving! Hope you are having a good one.

I drove to Oklahoma, then rode with family up to Branson, MO where we rented a lake cabin. The whole family is in the living room with their noisy kids, and I'm secluded in my bedroom. Isolation is bad—but being alone can be good.

Take care

August

To: *August_at_home*
From: *Allister_at_home*
Subject: RE: *Happy Thanksgiving*

November 23, 2018

Dear August,

Thanksgiving was spent with my step-dad's family—his sister and brother-in-law. It wasn't before long the brother-in-law spoke out of turn by saying, "Being gay is a choice!" This caused my mother to fill with silent rage and a desire to bury that man alive.

Sorry for the ranting.

Honestly, noisy kids and traveling in the car to the family cabin sounds like heaven!

Always,

Allister

15

At The Mercy of the Devil's Garment

"All right, I want you to cut out the pieces of the pattern you want to make and then pin them to the fabric. Let me know when you're done and I will check it for any changes the instructions may require," my mother instructed.

Suddenly, it was middle school home economics all over again. Flashbacks of my prepubescent years flashed across my mind—those awkward days from hell.

That was the last time I'd ever sewn something or touched the machine. It wasn't exactly a conquered skill as the sewing project was to make pillow. Not just any pillow, mind you. It was like some fun, cheap, precut, put-it-to-gether-in-minutes project. Mine was a yellow surfboard with a bold green stripe down the middle and two foot prints on the top of it.

Cute, right?

Another classmate[74] decided she was going to make the same one and when we finished our surfboards, hers looked awesome! Mine, however, looked like it had been attacked by a shark.

Like I said, sewing is not my strongest skill.

After cutting and pinning the necessary pattern pieces to the my awesome red stretchy fabric I purchased the week prior, my mother came into the kitchen and smoothed it all out while reading the ever confusing—more so than Ikea's—instructions.

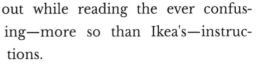

"Looks like piece #1 needs to be flipped so the printed side is laying facedown against the fold," she said, unpinning and repining it.

"Next, we are going measure the pieces that have grain lines."

"What the hell are grain lines?" I asked.

"They are the lines you can see on the pattern where you measure from the line to edge of the fabric. This will make it so that when you where it, the arms will not feel weird or out

---

[74] I cannot remember anyone's name from those days, even though they continued education with me all the way to high school. Her face is as clear as day, but her name is lost in a deep dense fog, forever lingering, trying to escape.

of place when you bend you arm," she explained.

It made sense, but at the same time, it didn't. My mother took a tape measure and with one of the patterns that had the grain line—in two areas, one at the very top and the other at the bottom—she promptly marked on the tape where the line needed to be with other.

It's a bit of a hassle after going through all the patterns and the process tends to be boring. But, it didn't take long to get everything ready for the final cut.

Removing the patterns from the cut fabric, I read the first step of the instructions.

—Take piece #4 and sew to piece #1.

DONE!

—Take piece #7 and sew to piece #3.

DONE!

—Take piece #6 and sew to piece #5

DONE!

—Take arm pieces and sew them to front and back of shirt.

I lined up the pieces like the picture showed, but they didn't match. What the hell? Moving them around, I found nothing matched.

I followed every the directions to a motherfucking T! There should be no reason it shouldn't match. When my mother took a look at it, she was just as baffled. Having someone who has been sewing since her early teenage years be just as clueless as I means I screwed it up way more than I realized.

I spent countless hours looking at what I did and the vague instructions. I recalled the scene from *Contact* and I wondered if I needed to think like Vegen? It made more sense to throw it all way and accept defeat. Instead, I cleaned it up and planned to tackle it again the next day.

"Just step away from it and come back to it another time," my mother suggested.

• • • • •

A week later, I picked up where I left off with my sewing project and attempted to figure out what went wrong.

Laying it out next to the instructions, I looked at the simple drawn out picture and noticed an S shape curve along the very top edge. Looking back at the real thing, it was far from that shape. I saw the start of the S, but half-way through it became a straight line going back up.

"Ohhhhhhhh, it's all making sense as to why the alignment is way off," I said to myself.

Grabbing the thread ripper, I began unstitching the sides of #1 and #3 and then resewed it all correctly. It took nearly two-and-half-hours to complete.

After that, all the pieces matched up perfectly!

Perfectly, I say!

I continued with the next step of the process, adding hems along the edges of the shirt bottom and sleeves until only the hood was left.

The one feature I wanted to add to make the workout

shirt unique was a zipper off to the side that opened up in the front. Calling my mother to ask how that could be achieved, she said, "all you have to do is cut a line right at the top where the neckline is and just a smidge before the zipper ends. Then fold in the sides and pin the zipper behind the so you're attaching and hemming at the same time."

Simple enough.

Doing as she said in a matter of minutes, the shirt was complete. Cutting off any long-hanging threads, and then washing the garment in cold water with a cup of white vinegar (to keep the dye in the fabric from bleeding), it was done and ready to worn.

That very same day, I took it out for a test run at my gym. The material moved great and offered no resistance. I received a few comments of how good it look from fellow gym members.

I was pretty proud that I was able to sew something and wear it out without it looking like my surfboard garbage from back in the day.

21. MAKE MY OWN CLOTHES

16

Skiing. I'm Going to Die

I pulled in to the Starbucks parking lot just before driving up the Mount Rose Highway where freshly fallen snow waited for me in Tahoe. I saw that Cyenna was already inside ordering her hot beverage while being her bubbly, energetic self and making the baristas laugh with her. It was amusing to see all this happening without sound. I could have dubbed their conversation into something inappropriate.

I had invited Cyenna to be my support for this glitter list item as I was deathly afraid of this particular activity:

Skiing.

Yes, I've lived in an area where skiing is the social norm

and people do it every winter. Let me give you a one-word explanation as to why I haven't done this: trees. When you hear about some random stranger dying after colliding with mother nature's air givers, well, you just don't bother.

Today, I plan to change that.

After putting my coffee order in and making small talk with the baristas, Cyenna and I climbed into my car and headed up the hill.

Checking the time—9:23 a.m.—I discovered we were actually going to arrive twenty minutes before my lesson started, which was at ten. I noticed Cyenna intensely grabbing the *oh shit handle* while her other hand clutched the seat belt.

I had to ask: "Everything okay?"

"Yes. No. You're taking the corners a little too fast," she confessed.

"Relax. I've been driving these hills for most of my driving life. Born and raised here, remember?" I said, assuring her.

She nodded, though she didn't budge. I felt kind of bad, but at the same time I was laughing and having a good time watching her fidget with fear. It's a good thing the drive wasn't that long.

Almost taking a wrong turn, a giant blue truck, who was in a hurry, honked at us to move out of the way as I entered the parking lot. Some people need to learn patience, especially in the snow—unless you want to end up with a fucked up car and visiting the hospital, calm the hell down.

Slowly heading down the first row of the parking lot, I saw it was packed full of Subarus.

"Ah, it must be lesbian ski day," I thought.

There were no close enough spots, which meant we had to hike to the lodge. Having not been to Tahoe for some time, I found the air crisp. I had overlooked how cold it can actually get, and since there was a snow storm the day before, today was extra cold. The view, though, made up for it.

Rays of sunshine travelled through the trees, glistening with freshly laid snow. Light whisperings of wind could be heard throughout the mountains, creating that eerie feeling. I've never been one for mountains, but I can see why people find it relaxing when enjoying nature.

Taking a few pictures of the scenery, Cyenna and I followed the icy path down to the lodge where two guys behind glass, much like when you go to the movie theater, sat and talked while waiting for something to do.

"Hi, yes, I purchased a ski lesson," I told the guy in the box.

"You're in the wrong spot, bro. Go inside and on the right you'll see stairs going down. You'll see a large sign with *lessons* on it. Can't miss it," he said with a smile.

"Okay, thank you."

Cyenna opened the door to the lodge and I stepped through first.

"All right, he said once we go in there should be stairs off to the right that go down."

And he was right. A large white square sign with blue lettering said, "Baskets, Rentals, & Lessons."

"This is it," I said, turning to Cyenna.

Following the arrow pointing down the stairs, I started to get nervous. I knew that once I went down there, I couldn't chicken out. Plus, I spent $115 on a non-refundable lesson. So, there's that too. There better be a really hot ski instructor waiting for me when I reach the bottom!

Nope.

Instead, there was a skinny, nineteen-year-old kid standing by a small pedestal who needed to pull his pants up.

"I'm here for the lesson that starts at ten," I said.

"Right over there," he said, pointing behind him.

Nodding my head, I headed over to the counter where a tall blonde woman wearing thick black glasses was waiting.

"Hi, I'm here for lessons."

"Is this your first time?" she asked.

"Would it be cliché to say…like a virgin?"

She laughed, shaking her head no. Handing her the ticket I printed back at home, it didn't take long to get checked in and get what I needed to pass "Go."

Cyenna followed me around the corner to a room filled

with silver boots from floor to ceiling on either side. In the middle I saw very large metal bench. If I didn't know any better, I would have thought I was inside a Foot Locker. Smelt like one, too. Any ideas I had about the Ski lodge—luxurious, sexy, extravagant—were now gone. The boot attendee handed me my request, and of course my big mouth opened up and said, "Do these come in Louis Vuitton?" Cyenna chuckled while the attendee ignored me and helped someone else.

Tough crowd.

After getting strapped in and walking around to make sure the boots weren't going to irritate me, granted they were heavy, they fit like a glove... or a boot, I should say. I forgot to purchase gloves before heading up, so I asked Cyenna if she could run up and purchase a pair with my debit card.

"All right, I'll be right back."

"Least expensive please," I said.

She threw a thumbs up in the air, letting me know she heard. Continuing onward, I now needed to get skis. The same guy who provided the boots already had two different skis ready for me.

"Here are two different sizes. Both are perfect for your height," he said, looking at me for a decision.

"Is there something one pair does that other doesn't do?" I asked.

"Not really. I would go with the shorter skis since this is your first time. It will be slower and help you turn better. Use longer if you're more experienced," he explained.

I wasn't entirely sure if what he was telling me was the

truth, but there wasn't enough time for me to Google the difference, so I decided to place blind faith in him and take the shorter skis. He then took the skis over to a guy who dressed like a sixteen-year-old; baggy pants, brightly colored belt, DC hat, and an oversized sweatshirt. For a moment, I thought I just met Benjamin Button, a young soul trapped in an older body. His deep-set wrinkles gave his age away.

Mr. Button placed the skis on his work bench and gave me a crash course.

"Basically, all you do is put the tip of the boot into the ski and press down with your heel. You'll hear a click that tells you it's secure."

He then took a screw driver and tightened some of the screws, ensuring that my rental wasn't going to fall apart on me while coming down the slope.

"One last thing, if you do fall and become unclipped, the ski has tiny brakes on the bottom to prevent them from sliding away down the hill," he said.

And here I had high hopes for a chase.

Either I am really not that funny, or this lodge is way too serious for my taste. Cyenna came around the corner holding a pair of black clothes. She had good timing because I needed somebody else to understand my dry sense of humor.

"You're all set. Do you have any questions?" he asked, locking eyes with me.

"Looks like I'm taken care of. Thank you."

Taking the baby skies, Cyenna and I made our way to the garage-looking door where the lessons were taking place. She handed back my debit card along with a new pair of gloves.

"The cheapest they had was $40," she said, concerned.

"Jeez! Oh well, that's the price I have to pay for waiting till the last minute," I said with disgust.

But Cyenna did good. All that was left was meeting my instructor for the next two hours. Cyenna and I parted ways as she went upstairs to the lodge for a drink. I walked toward a small group of four who would learn the basics with me.

The closer I got, the shorter my instructor became. So much for having an incredibly hot ski instructor! Instead, he was a fifty-something, short, overweight man who coached high school football and seemed to enjoy yelling.

"Thank you for finally joining us Mr. Dean," he said with a snarky tone.

"I do apologize," I said.

He returned to the lesson while shaking his head.

Out of fear and embarrassment, I didn't ask him to repeat what I missed. I figured I'd improvise when the time came.

After learning about turns, how to stop, leaning forward, and trusting our skis, the instructor felt we were ready to try the bunny hill.

I always imagined the bunny hill being much like the hill I visit whenever sledding becomes a reality. It's not very long but high enough to get some speed, and has fresh snow to break my fall when crashing is unavoidable.

I was wrong.

The Bunny slope is an almost level hill with no fresh

snow anywhere. It's also cluttered with children and older folks who constantly fall.

Off to the side, there was a people mover ramp like the one you would find in the airport—you know, the small strip you step on to so you don't have to walk anymore—leading up to the top of the small hill.

"Now, when you get to the very top, you have to hop onto the snow. Otherwise, the ramp will abruptly stop and the operators will have to reset it," our instructor said.

I didn't believe him until the escalating ramp stopped because someone didn't hop onto the snow, causing all of us simultaneously whiplash forward.

"They seriously need to figure out a better way for people to transition from the ramp to the snow!" I loudly said.

One of the people in my class behind me, Sarah, agreed with me. With both of us laughing, we made small introductions. Sarah is a stay at home wife of a fireman who is learning to ski for the first time while her five-year-old son is already a pro. She pointed him out and we watched as he owned the powder. Even though it was just the Bunny slope, her son made it his bitch.

At the top of the ramp, we hopped onto the snow just and waited for our teacher and the remainder of our class.

"All right class, we are going to learn to stop, turn, and not fall."

"I'm gonna fall," I confirmed with Sarah.

Heading down the hill first, my feet were locked in a permanent pizza shape, keeping me from picking up any speed. I was just gliding down stiff a board.

"Allister, get out of pizza position and start turning!" my

instructor yelled.

"Is he crazy?" I said to myself, raising a thumb in the air.

Switching from pizza to French fry, my slow glide increased to power-walking speed. Bending my knees a little more, I turned my left ski in so I would turn right, and then turned my right ski in to go left.

Wasn't so bad.

Until a little girl skied her way into my path, not paying any attention.

I quickly changed to pizza position but it wasn't slowing me down enough. My first time skiing and this is what happens. Colliding with a little girl isn't what I had in mind for today, so I did the only thing that came to mind...

"Move bitch!" I screamed.

Upon hearing me, the girl scurried out of my path, unsure of how take the insult. In my defense, I would never call a little girl a bitch, but in the moment it just spilled from my lips and got her to move.

At the bottom, I turned around and saw that Sarah was right behind me, attempting to do turns while trying not to fall. One by one, everyone else from the class—including the instructor—headed down the slope, either about to eat shit or collide with another skier.

Thankfully, none of that happened.

"You all did great! Ready to tackle the blue slope?" the

instructor asked.

The group (including myself) was in an agreement to move on to level two. Mimicking our instructor, we detached from our skies, carrying them up a small hill where we attached them again and waited our turn in line for the lift.[75]

"Us three will share a lift while you, Allister, will share one with Sarah behind us."

No complaints there.

"When we get to the top, all you do is bend your knees and push forward. If you don't, you'll get sucked back into the lift and you'll be heading back down."

What's with the disclosure—we're not complete idiots! It's a damn lift for Christ's sake.

As we headed up the hill in our floating cabled taxi, my lift buddy and I decided it was the time to make small talk.

"So Sarah, what's it like being a stay at home mom?" I asked.

"Boring! I love my child and all, but it's just the same the thing everyday. The only thing that keeps me going is the play dates with the other moms on my street," Sarah explained.

"Social interaction, I understand," I empathized.

"I could care less about the interaction with the other moms. It's just an excuse to day drink and have other peoples' kids keep my mine entertained for a couple of hours!"

Laughing at her response, I couldn't believe how much

---

[75] Seems tedious if you ask me. Why not just ski over to the lift? I don't think this instructor even knows what he's doing!

of a wino this mom was. There was a reason she and I connected! Us wino's have to stick together.

"Are those Versace sunglasses?" a lift worker screamed.

"I think he's talking to you," Sarah said.

I saw a young man sitting inside a little shack with a little heater in the corner. It tried to keep him warm, but I doubted it was doing the job.

"No, they're fake." I replied.

A disappointed expression came over his face. Then, just before getting off the lift, the young man wished us a happy ski day.

"You should have said they were," Sarah said.

"Why? They're not," I said.

"He doesn't know that. Plus, you saw how sad he was."

"I know! Usually, when I disappoint someone, it's when I tell a guy no to a date."

Sarah laughed.

Meeting up with the rest of the group in an open clearing, our instructor said that we would be heading down the hill on a path he pointed at. It was inclined much more than the bunny slope, and by the looks of it, didn't have any fresh snow.

"Let's practice our turns!" the instructor yelled.

"I'm gonna die!" I said to myself.

"Come on, Allister! Race you down," Sarah said, gliding past me.

Is this chick buzzed? Wouldn't put it past her. Pushing myself forward with my poles, I instantly went into pizza mode.

"You're not gonna catch up to her if you do that."

Looking over my right shoulder, I saw my instructor skiing beside me, shooting me a look of sheer encouragement.

He was right.

Fuck it!

If I crash and end up in the hospital, at least I can say I tried. Shifting my feet into French fry mode, my speed went from a safe gliding to shredding fast.

"I'm coming for you, girl!" I yelled.

There was no one in front of me, so it was the perfect opportunity to practice turning without the fear of colliding into another human—unlike earlier. I still couldn't believe that little girl just stopping in the middle of slope. That tells me what kind of driver she'll end up being in the future.[76]

Turning left, then right, I began to pick up speed. My fear slowly melted away, shaping into pure fun. What was I so afraid before? If anything went wrong to the point of losing control, I'd just fall over.

Passing by Sarah, she screamed, "Ski, Forrest, Ski!"

Now all I needed was a backpack full of wine and I'd be set to ski for hours. Getting tipsy while shredding snow down a mountain probably wasn't the best idea, but whatever.

Making it to the bottom, I was overwhelmed with a rush. I could now understand why people love doing this! The other skiers from my class made it to bottom, one by one. Sarah slid next to me and gave me a high-five. Cyenna

---

[76] Should I take down that little girls information and let DMV know for when the times comes?

came over from the lodge, yelling with excitement and waving her hands in the air.

"That was so awesome! I saw you coming down, totally owning the hill."

"I know, right? I just embraced my fear and let go of it!" I said, matching her excitement, "Let's get a quick photo and grab something to eat. Shredding the hill really made me famished!"[77]

~~1. LEARN TO SKI~~

---

[77] I achieved skiing before being admitted to the hospital—hence no beard.

To: *August_ at_ home*
From: *Allister_ at_ home*
Subject: *Merry Xmas*

December 25, 2018

Dear August,

Just got your Christmas card—after not checking my mail-box for couple of days. Hopefully, you'll get mine soon as I sent mine out a tad late. But anywho, Merry Christmas!

Today, my folks and I are going out for breakfast to Hash House A Go-Go. The last time I was there, it was in San Diego with an old flame four years ago. Their alternative eggs benny is simply wonderful! If you haven't gone, make it a point to do so when you're near one.

What's interesting about this 25th is that my youngest brother is meeting us at Hash. The last time I spoke to him was when I had pneumonia, and seven years before that. Not only will my mother and I spend Christmas morning with him, but this is the first time Tom—our step-dad—and my brother are meeting. I'm not sure what to expect honestly. Keep you posted!

Always,

Allister

December 25, 2018

Hi Allister,

Merry Christmas! There is still 55 more minutes of it in Oklahoma.

I love Hash House—it was the one place I missed hitting up last time I was in Reno .

So how did the family debut go?

There was a time when I had four or more Christmas's to go to each year: Mom's, Dad's, Mema G, and Grandpa T. This year there was only one and it was so much more relaxed.

No one got uptight over the gay issue and I had no pit in my stomach because of any particular people I really didn't want to be around. There were no guilt trips and no Debbie Downers who can't let a day go by without playing the victim of the entire world...it was nice.

We did Christmas on Christmas Eve, and since this morning there wasn't much to do, I went and volunteered downtown. It felt good getting involved. I kinda had an unrealistic expectations to be moved in someway but I wasn't. There was a constant line of families moving through who were less fortunate. I hate that word but I can't think of a better descriptor. I think the presence of white, middle class (or upper) guilt was notable—I'm totally guilty, too. People made sure to dress casual—but nice-casual—and maybe spent more time on their hair so as to give the appearance of a volunteer, not an attendee. Got some uncomfortable looks from being around poor people. It felt awkward for the first 20 minutes, and then it was fine. Since the whole thing was volunteer driven, it took you that much time to figure out where the help was needed. I'd totally do it again.

I've started therapy, not sure why (have a vague idea), but, I'm trying online therapy with a gay therapist. I like it.

I got caught up reading four books at once—I'm about to finish *Brutally Bitter* as the last book of the year. One resolution last year was to read 12 books in 12 months, and I made it happen. Next year I am resuming my MBA so I'll have to scale it down or count my textbooks, too.

Talk soon, hope you had a great day!

August

17

Meanwhile...On The Hunt For A Tuxedo

"I need a tuxedo!"

I threw my hands up in the air as an associate came rushing over to help. Cyenna looked around at the other shoppers who stared at me, not sure of what was going on.

"For New Year's Eve, I presume?" the Express associate asked with a smirk.

"Oh, I can see why they hired you," I sarcastically replied.

"We have a few over here."

She pointed to the back of the store and escorted us over. The employee pulled two different types of suits off the rack and held them up side by side. One jacket was a nasty, wine crushed velvet ensemble and the other really had nothing special going for it. Almost didn't look like a tux, and it didn't scream, HAPPY NEW YEAR!

"Do you have one that's blue with black satin lapels?" I asked.

"Sorry, these are the only two we have. They didn't send us very much."

"How disappointing," I said, looking over at Cyenna.

My inner Miranda—from the Devil Wears Prada—started to emerge. Cyenna was on the same page, shaking her head no for both suits.

"Well, thanks anyways."

"Let me know if you need anything else," the associate said, hanging the items back on the rack.

Cyenna and I started to head out of the store, talking up how ugly the suits were, when a shiny, glittery item caught her eye. Mid-step, she bolted away from me, but I unknowingly carried on the conversation by myself like a crazy person.

"Wait!" Cyenna said.

Turning around, I saw her hold up a dress with such excitement, mouthing the words "New Year's," then pointing at herself. The dress was long-sleeved and cut just above the knee. It was black with skewed metallic rectangles running throughout the dress. Light netting was used in between the metallic pieces, giving it an almost peek-a-book look.

"Did you want to try it on?"

"Fuck yeah!" she said, sprinting to the dressing room.

Waiting in the echoey dressing room of mirrors, I could hear her removing her everyday clothes and slipping on the dress. Then the rummaging fell silent.

"How does it look?" I asked.

"It's not too bad. I need to lose a bit of weight," she told me.

"Come out and let's see?"

"No!" she yelled.

"Why? It probably looks amazing! Quit putting yourself down!"

"I don't know."

Without any sort of warning, I got down on my hands and knees and peering up from under the door. "The dress looks amazing on you! You're going to turn heads!" I excitedly said.

She screamed.

"Oh, come on, it's not like I haven't seen titties before, and I'm certainly not getting any pleasure from this."

"I know, but still," she said, covering herself.

"Sweetie, remember I like cock just as much as you do. Anyways, you look fucking hot! And if you don't buy that dress, I'm going to have to wear it out myself."

"Okay, Okay I'll get it. Now get up so I can get dressed," she said shaking her hands at me.

At the register, Cyenna pulled out the price tag to see how much damage the metallic dress was going to do: $180. We both looked at each other with disgust. The same employee—who had shown us the ugly suits—rung us up and said that the dress was on sale for $50.

"Jackpot!" Cyenna said, whipping out her credit card and holding it in the air.

"Before you swipe your card, what about this tag?" I

said.

A small tag fell off the dress that read, "THIS ITEM CANNOT BE RETURNED IF THIS TAG IS REMOVED." Such a deal breaker for those who wear dresses one night and return them the next. What if the dress was too big for her by New Years? Looking at the Express employee, we noticed a look of worry plastered across her face. She pressed a button on her black radio cord for assistance.

"Helen? What do I do about this tag that just came off... Yeah, that one. Okay, let me see if I can find it," she said.

The employee rummaged through items below the counter and couldn't find what she was looking for. I don't think she knew what she was looking for either. Luckily for her, I had a bit of retail experience and knew what needed to be done.

"Sweetie, I think that's what you're looking for," I said, pointing to a small item tucked away in a white box behind her.

Turning around, she pulled out the small garment-tagging gun. It had a thin metal needle at the tip, and when the trigger was squeezed, it released a small plastic fastener that attached a tag onto a garment.

"I really don't know how to work one of these," she said.

"Give it here, I'll show you," I said, grabbing all three items.

"First, slip the tag hole on the metal tip of the gun and then poke the inside tag of the dress with the gun." I pulled the trigger, and CLICK, the tag was secured to the dress. Folding the dress neatly and placing it in the bag, I turned to Cyenna and said, "And thank you for shopping at Express, please see us soon again."

Cyenna busted up laughing. She was just as amazed as the register girl on how I did all of that. I half-expected them to start clapping.

"You pick up a few things when you've been in retail," I said, leading the way out the store.

Cyenna and I rode an escalator in J. C. Penny up to the men's department. The last suit I purchased came from this very store and served its purpose for the last five years. I was a bit sad because Express didn't have a selection beyond the *Austin Powers* crushed velvet collection. I expected better really, but as a warrior of fashion, I'll never give up until the Hero Garment is found.

Reaching the top, we found the department was silent. Dead silent. Even the people working there pretended to look busy when the tables and displays looked amazing. That meant I didn't have to become Brad Pitt and do the whole fight club thing between the aisles.

"What exactly are you looking for, Allister?" Cyenna asked, sorting through the racks of suits.

"A blue tux, but not just any blue; a royal blue with black satin on the lapels. I saw one on Pinterest and knew I wanted to ring in the New Year in it."

"You mean like this one?"

Cyenna walked over to a display where a male mannequin was dressed in a blue tux. "Well, that didn't take long," I said. I walked over to the display and examined the hell out of the suit. Touching, feeling, and yes, rubbing the material. The color wasn't exactly royal blue, but a deep blue color with a slight black pattern overlay. I glanced around to see if any other choices were available—sadly again, no.

"All right, this is going to be it. Let's get my size and try this bad boy on!" I told her.

Judging from all the sizes the jacket came in, I figured the store must have just gotten it. Grabbing a 44R in length, I made my way to the nearby dressing room. The brand was the same as my first suit at home, so the jacket should fit just right. But since I didn't want to make two trips, I tried it on. Cyenna quietly stood by the mannequin.

"Are you wanting to get to know the mannequin? If not, then come with me to the dressing room!" I said grabbing her by the arm.

"He isn't my type and wait, am I allowed to go in there?" she asked.

"There is an area for you to sit in and it's like a giant closet with individual rooms. You won't see anyone changing. Plus, there's no one here. The store is ours!"

"I just don't want to get into trouble," Cyenna said, looking around.

"Doubt they'll care."

Dragging her to the men's fitting room, Cyenna peered around the corner to make sure no one else was around. Rolling my eyes, I walked over to the three-way mirror and removed my beige trench and cardigan. I placed the nude hanger on a wooden hook attached to wall and slipped the tuxedo jacket on. The color was amazing on me but felt really loose. The jacket was two sizes too big! The sleeve length was perfect though, everywhere else just had huge pockets of space.

"Hey, can you grab me a 40R, love," I said.

"Yea," she replied.

Maybe tuxedos fit differently than regular suit jackets? Strange, a jacket is a jacket in my book. Cyenna came around the corner with the 40R size. Swapping the 44R with the new size, I quickly put it on. Better, but still big.

"Cyenna, 38R and 36R please."

"Are you sure? Those are pretty small sizes," questioning she said.

"I'm sure."

Handing her the 40R, I was starting to get worried. What if the jacket wasn't made slim fit? What were my other options? Ordering online at a whole other store and putting complete faith that what they tell you is slim fit is such a hassle and a chore itself. So, that'd be out of the question.

"Here is a 36R and a 38R," she said coming around the corner of the dressing room.

"It's going to be such a letdown if both of these jackets don't work. Might have to write a letter to the designer explaining how he sucks at tuxedos," I said.

Cyenna giggled and watched the mirror's reflection as I tried on the 38R first. Way better! The jacket though, still had a minor gap where the button sat. Everywhere else fit snuggly. Trying on the 36R next, Cyenna crossed her fingers and bit her bottom lip in hopes that this size was going to be the one that put our worries to rest. Slipping on and buttoning the jacket, I took a deep breath.

"How does it feel?" Cyenna asked.

"It fits perfectly!" I said with a huge grin.

I ran my hands over front and back of the jacket and

gazed into the mirror. All I could say was, DAMN! I looked good. All that was missing was a Walther PPK with a silencer and I would be set to become the next James Bond.

Hanging the 36R jacket back on the hanger, we shopped for the rest of the outfit: a bowtie, blue lapel hand-kerchief, a white button up shirt, and black oxford shoes. The total came to a whopping $200. Impressed with my shopping skills, the cashier informed me before sliding my card through the machine that the day before the suit was only 40% off and that today it was now 50% off. This day kept getting better! First, it was Cyenna's dress discount, and now my suit had a discount, too! The shopping gods totally had our backs.

With the Hero Garment in hand, we headed out of J. C. Penney and back into the mall.

"What do you want to do next?" Cyenna asked.

"Celebrate of our finds over cosmos and lunch?" I suggested.

"FUCK YES!" she said, running to the Cheesecake Factory and leaving me behind.

My Twenties

My Twenties

AU REVOIR!

For the last ten years, you've taught me right from wrong and helped me become the person I am. Although there has been an atrocious amount of ups and downs—some caused by me—I wouldn't have changed anything. How else am I to maintain my wise *Yodaness* if I have nothing to look back on?

Recently, I confessed a lot to an old friend—while I may or not have been completely drunk—saying that, "Yes, I indeed fucked up my friendships and I'm now getting what's been coming to me." Part of this was a huge burden I needed to get off my chest, realizing how unimportant those friendships were to me, and that I'm grateful to have him be the recipient of my mini-meltdown at two in the morning, which including him telling me what I needed to hear about old friends that have already gone down the road I'm traveling myself.

The best way to describe this is showing up to a party thinking that you're not going to know anybody until you recognize someone in a sea of faces.

Pulling an Elsa and letting it go, I decided it was the right thing to do and it was a healthy approach for entering the next stage of my life. Otherwise, it'll be just as chaotic.

Always,

Allister

To: *August_ at_ home*
From: *Allister_ at_ home*
Subject: *Happy New Year*

January 1, 2019

Dear August,

Happy New Year!

Hopefully, you spent the evening with good friends!

I shared the evening with two friends that soon became just one. Samantha and her boyfriend decided to head to the next town over and an hour and half prior to midnight. Which was fine, I wasn't upset. But I was glad she made it to the bar and spent a couple of hours hanging out.

I wore my fabulous blue tux that not only drew stares from gay men, but straight women as well. Growing the beard was the cherry on top because a couple straight guys admired it and even asked to touch it. Christina couldn't believe it either! The crowd was vibrantly active, and when I say that, I mean the majority of straight men had their shirts off, giving laps dances to anyone who wanted one.

One thing I've never done is the New Years Eve midnight kiss. Yes, I'm almost thirty and never have done that. Until now! Throughout the night, my two friends—including Samantha's boyfriend—were hot the prowl with me to find a guy I was going to give my kiss to. There were a few, but none that really had my interest. I know, I know it's just a kiss.

I decided to be very bold that night—mind you I only had one Cosmopolitan, so alcohol was not a factor—and introduced myself to a young guy of merely twenty-one who does makeup at Dillards. He was cute, and perfect for the occasion. But, I guess it was a green light for him to keep kissing me from then on after midnight.

Here's where the night got interesting.

Closer to midnight, my past found themselves in the same bar. Old friends that I'd cut out of my life back when I was twenty-five. They hadn't seen me with a beard and I thought it might help conceal my identity—to keep the

peace, of course.

It didn't.

The group of ex-friends quickly realized I was present, and one of them made a point to walk circles around me to get a closer look.

One of those friends, who I stay in contact with and manage to hang out with from time to time, came over and had a quick conversation with me. He was drunk and spilled more information as to why mending friendships wasn't going to happen. (A year ago I reached out to see if it was possible, but heard nothing in response.)

"Andy doesn't want to make amends with you, nor does Dalton." Those were his exact words. My response, I felt was appropriate, "That's okay. I don't expect them to. We were all young and dumb. I personally took their friendship for granted and I'm now paying the price for it. I've accepted it and moved on. The last few years have been rough, but it's starting to turn around for me. It's not even 2019 and great things are already happening."

That friend just stood in front of me, not sure of how to respond. But, I had more to say.

"And that's why it's going to be very hard for me to say this. I do love you Galen, but you and I can no longer be friends. You're torn between your current friends who were part of my life but now are my past. That's not fair to you. We are in very different parts of our life; I'm progressing and you're standing still. I cannot do that. So, after tonight we should part ways, leaving on good terms. It's for the best and I've thought this through more than you'll ever know."

He nodded, shook my hand, and walked back to his group. Christina, who was next me, couldn't believe what she just witnessed. Like I said, it was very hard to cut the cord of friendship with someone who was a good part of my twenties, but it wasn't healthy for me in end. I don't regret making that decision.

Big news! Almost forgot to mention it. There is a website that an author friend of mine suggested I "sink my teeth into" as he put it, to help build my writing portfolio as well as getting my name out there—writersworks.com. After taking a look, it's pretty much like indeed.com but reverse. You build a profile and publications seek out writers based on that said profile.

Well, I've been hired to write an article...

Dear Allister,

We've come across your profile and love what we see! Here at ********.com we would like to hire you for a piece, "What to do when you've broken trust in your relation-

ship." Please reach out regarding any questions you might have.

Thanks.

It's right up my alley—relationships/love and the pay is pretty decent. I'm going to accept the offer, but the only problem is that I personally have never broken trust, which means I'm going to have to go out, get into a relationship, and break his trust.

Do you think it's a good idea? Using someone like that or do you think I should just decline the offer?

Always,

Allister

P.S. I now get to cross two things off my glitter list!

~~26. NEW YEARS IN STYLE~~
~~29. NEW YEARS MIDNIGHT KISS~~

To: *Allister_at_home*
From: *August_at_home*
Subject: RE: *My New Years Resolutions*

January 6th, 2019

Hi Allister!

Happy New Year!

I am just getting over being sick. It kicked in the evening of 1/1—NOT how I wanted to spend the first part of the year. My aunt had it over Christmas, then my mom got it. I think I got something much different, though: a case of food poisoning from a fast food restaurant I stopped at on the way back to Texas. I was throwing up like Linda Blair in The Exorcist! I did at least enjoy the 12 preceding days off work in good health and that was fun. I did a WHOLE bunch of nothing. Hung out with my mom and step dad, saw my grandmother, my brother, and his family.

On New Year's Eve I spent some time with Kory, my best gay friend since I was 16. We actually dated for about five minutes way back then and fooled around, and then we were roommates for 2 years. I could never imagine us as anything more than Golden Girl sisters though. The idea of sex with Kory seems incestuous.

Anyway, I had grown concerned because none of my calls, texts, or facebook messages to Kory had been getting returned. I reached out to his husband (they are legally married) who told me, "if you want to say hi to Kory, I'd suggest you try to reach out yourself ☺." Shit. I realized he must be pissed at me for something I didn't even know about.

I reached out to a mutual friend and was like "not trying to gossip, but what the hell is going on?"
She said I was the only one she trusted enough to tell that Kory and his husband were on the rocks. After a few years of marriage, his husband moved out and Kory wasn't taking it well. Also, his phone had been broken for months and he'd been using AOL instant messenger (which I thought was extinct) on his iPad.

I messaged him and heard back saying—yes, come over!

So I did. His apartment is in the ghetto, but it's really the culturally funky and arguably gay hipster part of NW Oklahoma City (OKC). He'd been cleaning all day and it still looked like an episode of hoarders. Apparently, he had been rebelling against his soon to be ex-husband the neat freak by having shit strewn everywhere and not caring about it. Kory is a theater director and big time into art, so various art projects and supplies littered the apartment.

Also—he now has like 3 other people living in his apartment. Two of them look shay-to-the-D. A third guy comes over briefly. He's polite, but his appearance jars me. They briefly go into the other room, then the guy says goodbye and leaves.
Adding to the ghetto-ness of it all, Kory asked me to turn on the lamp. I do, and nothing comes on. "Son of a bitch! I'm going to have to find a working lightbulb!" He proceeds to go to the stove, takes the light out of the oven, and plugs it in. I burst into laughter, "That is SUCH a crackhead move—

you should move to Reno!"

"No, it's not, it's a poor thing—not a crackhead thing!"
One of his roommates brought home a straight boy he met at the Circle K on 39th (the gay district). I thought "Uhm-mm hello—every gay ever in OKC knows anyone loitering around the Circle K on 39th is a male prostitute!"

Kory wants Kool Aid and boxed wine and the ghettoness continues. (Actually, I am making fun here but he revels and embraces everything about him that's ghetto. He also has more wit and a sharper tongue than anyone I have ever met which is why I have always loved him. I have seen him chew up and spit out more than a few piss-elegant queens who thought they were God's gift. He's really a riot.)

I kinda wanted to get out of the apartment and wind down our visit because honestly, I was a little uncomfortable.

So, the kid who I think is a male prostitute needed a ride to the nearest store a couple blocks down, and Kory told him to come with us—I am VERY nervous at this point. Apparently, the kid was from very rural southeastern Oklahoma (about 2 hours away) and had become separated from his party and had to have a relative drive up to collect him. He had spent the night walking around town until he bumped into Kory's roommate—a total stranger—who just invited him over.

I was nervous about anything I had placed in the backseat

of my car getting stolen, but more so (assuming the worst) about this kid's mom flying off the handle and possibly accosting me and yelling, "What did you do to my baby??" This kid was legal, but a teenager. It's just how I pictured it all going down. Fortunately, his mom (I think she was a lesbian) was as sweet as could be. She thanked us and asked for directions back to the interstate.

In an awkward, very young, way this kid was nice, too. He had a chubby cowboy look to him. He thanked me a few times for giving him a ride that was only a 2-3 block walk.

After he got out, I said, "Kory! You know he was a PROSTI-TUTE!?"

"No, he was NOT. He was nice and he's too fat to be a hooker! He was just a nice, stranded, kid."

I thought about it and realized he was right. I had been holding him at an arm's length, not talking much and trying to be mysterious in case I suddenly had to start fighting or throw him out. I could now see that I had really misjudged the situation. Thankfully, I didn't put my foot in my mouth at any point, but I felt like a jerk for making assumptions about this poor teenager who had been stranded, broke, and cellphone-less on the street for 24 hours. I should have regarded him with more charity.

My guess was he was awkward because he was either a not-yet-out-of-the-closet kid trying to escape rural Oklahoma

208 } ALLISTER DEAN

via the OKC gay district, or he really might have been straight—all he did was talk about cars and country music. Also, maybe he had never seen gay people before?

Anyway, the night progressed, and I took Kory to the store for his Kool Aid and Boxed Wine. He forgot his ID, and even though he's 42, the clerk wouldn't sell it to him. The clerk wouldn't sell it to me with my valid ID because it had become clear who the real buyer was. Finally, we got into a different line and just successfully made the transaction.

Kory told me about an underground venture he's got going on: he's buying syringes in bulk for like $11 a case because junkies will pay $5 a needle, and so will dealers. It turns out I was right about the scary but somewhat polite guy I met in his apartment. Yup, he's a dealer. Kory persuaded me to go to the south-side's House of Pain, a novelty shop where meth heads buy their glass pipes. He wanted to buy whippets (the aerosol cartridges people can get a quick high from by inhaling). I was was kind of curious to see if he was fibbing to me. Seriously, we did that in high school—it's the equivalent of sucking on a whipped cream can.

Anyway, as tragic as it sounds, part of the reason we've been friends for so long is because EVERYTHING is an adventure. One night, during one of our trips to a sex club in Dallas, he broke his ankle while running and falling after a drunk homeless man outside pulled his dick out and demanded a blowjob while Kory was getting something out of the car. In his haste, not only did he break his ankle (which he was too drunk to realize until the next day), but he also locked my keys in the car at 3 a.m. outside a sketchy gay bar in a shitty part of Dallas.

He broke the news to me just as I made my way into the upper echelon of circle jerks featuring some hot college guys. (I was thin in my college days, but in that environment I was still a B+ trying to weasel my way into a sleazy A+ quality crowd.) It really was good seeing him, but I may keep some boundaries from here on out.

I LOVE that blue tux—very fancy! Thank you for the card. It was very nice of you and the kind words mean so much.

Congrats on your offer! To be honest, go for it! Remember, you're doing things that you normally wouldn't ever do and if this is to help build your portfolio in the long run, then this guy is nothing. Do it!

Take care,

August

18

Swipe Right Party

"Do you already have Tinder downloaded?" Olivia asked.

"I don't," I responded while pouring wine for invited guests.

"This feels like *How to Lose A Guy in 10 Days*," Brian said.

He was right; this had Kate Hudson written all over it. Taking the advice of my pen pal, this was just going to be a transaction—nothing more, nothing less. Plus, since I'm looking at three more years of college in my future, I might as well start building my portfolio. Olivia and Brian[78] didn't hesitate after I told them about my assignment. They actually encouraged me and helped me find the *guy* I was going to use.

---

[78] FYI: Brian is a long term friend who is well versed in the gay community. So, his expertise was appreciated.

"We've got wine and snacks now, so let's find Mr. Right!" Brian announced.

"Well, Mr. For-How-Long-It-Lasts," I said, correcting him.

Brian mentioned beforehand that Tinder was full of guys who were ready to mingle, so it was just going to take some time to go through them. We all agreed that it had to be someone who:

- was looking for an honest relationship
- didn't have an ego, and
- was *authentic.*

After downloading the so-called dating app, my two close friends built my profile. Brian had said that everyone should have good friends create your dating profile because they know you best—which I feel is true.

Describing oneself can only go so far until arrogance takes over.

"All we need is a picture...oh hot damn! Modest guys in their birthday suits!" Brian said, rapidly scrolling through and zooming on a few pictures in my camera role.

"What? I'm single! My sex life is on a natural hiatus, and so...I need...visual stimulation," I said trying to grab my phone back.

Olivia was faster and she snatched my phone out of Brian's hand.

"Just saying you have good taste in men and wine. I'm really enjoying the wine you brought over, Allister. It means you have standards," Brain said, complimenting me.

"I like this photo," Olivia said.

"Which one?" I asked.

"Black and white, your head resting on your hand on that chair, the one where your hair is on point."

There was no need for Olivia to show me what she was uploading because I approved.

After reviewing the profile, I had to say it was the best profile that was ever constructed, except for one thing.

"I don't have an AA in Fine Arts. I dropped out years ago, remember? Wish I hadn't because I was just shy of completing it," I said.

"What part of breaking trust don't you understand? You're going to lie about it and get caught," Olivia said with a smirk.

She was right, lying can easily break trust. But, I have a terrible poker face and I wouldn't do so well at the card table. I'd probably lose not only all my money, but a leg, an arm, and my soul.

Olivia, Brian, and I took turns going through each of the profiles that appeared on my screen. For every five profiles that we swiped left for no, one would get swiped right. The dating pool was huge, but the guys lacked depth. Most of them were early twenty-something guys who looked like they lied all the time to get what they want. The guy I needed had to be in his late twenties to early thirties and be ready to find love.[79]

"Soooooooooo many guys. I bet we've only swiped right on like...four already," Olivia moaned.

---

[79] I'm thirty and I don't even know what it means. Don't think anyone does, regardless of age.

"What about him?" I asked.

"Um. No. He's a hairdresser who's new to town. His boyfriend caught him having an orgy in his living room. He's not the one," Brian gossiped.

"Keeping trying! There's bound to be one decent fish in this school of fish!" confidently I said.

Brian rolled his eyes and held out his wine glass, indicating he needed a refill. After pouring more Merlot for the lush, he handed my phone back to me because it was my turn to swipe through the next thousand guys.

At ten o'clock, we finally reached the end of the never ending list of profiles. All the profiles we collectively swiped right on received mutual swipes minutes after. Brian took control of all the conversations that poured in. One by one, we realized most were chock full of egotism.

"This guy looks promising," Brian said, handing over my phone.

"Yeah?" Taking the phone, I saw the message read, "What was your last adventure?"

Olivia was also impressed by the message.

"Clark is 27 and works in education. His Instagram shows he just travelled to Greece and it appears he's been single for a while. Looks like he's what you're looking for, sweetie," Olivia said with a smile.

I responded to Clark with my Folsom Street Fair story, knowing full well he would be intrigued to hear about the details.[80] Within a few minutes, Clark was hooked.

---

[80] As predicted, Clark was intrigued. I had a feeling I was going to read this kid like a book. Hate when I stumble upon a predictable person.

"So?" Olivia asked while Brian stared.

"We found ourselves a winner, ladies and gent...well ladies," I confirmed, making fun of Brian in the process.

"Thank god, I was about to give up on this party and hit up Faces for better excitement," Brian said, sassing me.

"Come on now, how many of us gays that you know of can say they experienced something like this?"

Brian smirked.

"That's what I thought, now we charm him and get our first date scheduled," I said.

"Charm him then, Mr. Love," Olivia said.

As I said goodbye to my helpers and cleaned up the empty wine bottles they neglected to help with, despite helping me consume their contents, it was up to me now to secure a date and start a relationship that would only result in a tragic end.

What had I gotten myself into?

19

Timeline of Clark: Part I

JANUARY 11TH

Met up with Clark a day before our initial date. He found a way to touch my arm and kiss me in the parking lot. Hours later we had dinner and then went to karaoke at a nearby gay bar. Come to find, out we have a mutual sex partner— that person walked into the gay bar. I told Clark before hand that I haven't had sex in three years—another lie. It'd only be a matter of time before he dug deep into my Insta- gram account to discover it was mid-last year when I had sex. Night ended well.

JANUARY 12TH

Had dinner with him again, and this time we ended up at a bowling alley. After two games, we both admitted to throwing the game letting each other win. Made our way to the University as he questioned me about my degree in Fine Arts—Olivia's lie worked. We shared an intense kissing session on campus.

JANUARY 15TH

Had drinks at one of my favorite bars late at night. Clark told me about the huge scar he has on his waist from getting surgery to remove excess skin after losing tons of weight. Told me it looked like he'd been sawed in half during a magic show—kudos for a good joke. At that moment, I felt that since he shared something personal with me, I should share something personal with him. I got him hooked but at the same time felt really bad for what he was about to go through.

JANUARY 18TH

Clark reserved a hotel room for my 30th birthday and provided a BJ as a gift (which was absolutely terrible—sloppy is all I can say about that) before meeting up with his friends at a bar where Monique Hart was performing.[81] His friends are utter losers and don't really have lives. We went back to the hotel to wake up early for the women's march the next day.

---

[81] Don't get me wrong, RuPaul is fun, but gets old real fast.

20

A Hidden
Pussy Agenda

The day after my 30th birthday—which was nothing but Clark doing what he wanted to do, we found ourselves downtown heading up main street to the city's arch where his friends were waiting for us—along with many, many, many women who gathered, most holding picket signs.

Today was the annual Women's March.

Last year, I had heard about this event through a friend who shared stories such as the attendees wearing oversized vagina hats. It sounded like an event I had to see for myself.

"Hey girls!" Clark's friend Adam said.

After greeting and exchanging pleasantries with Adam and his boyfriend James, we all stood in the crisp, cold January weather while waiting for more people to arrive. Some of the picket signs were interestingly funny, and most of them were about President Trump and how horrible and terrible he was as a leader and a person.

"I should bring a sign next year. I just don't know what it should say," Adam said.

"Even though I like cock, I respect the pussy," I shouted.

Clark and his friends laughed. As more and more people gathered, a couple of public speakers with megaphones expressed their thoughts about women's rights and how us being there was making a change, even though I really didn't think I was making any sort of difference other than providing a larger headcount for the cause.

Fifteen minutes later, a woman with a megaphone stood in front what was now a massive crowd and spoke about how women have come so far and were still fighting, causing everyone to become pumped up. I, on the other hand, really didn't pay attention because I was on the hunt to find the vagina hats my friend mentioned, but I saw nothing of the sort.

The woman with the megaphone abruptly ended her speech, and people slowly began to walk forward. Honestly, this event was a total bust as the sidewalks were still clear.

"Down with Trump!" a disembodied voice screamed.

Looking around to see who blurted out their internal, immature feelings, nobody in the crowd stood out like a sore thumb or had regrettable expression. This began feeling more like a Hate Trump Rally than a women's march— can you say tacky? If this was the only reason people came out to march, then excuse me as I bee-line out of the crowd and into a restaurant for lunch; I'm on the verge of becoming a savage animal!

Coming to the end of main street, the crowd shifted left toward an open concrete quad that had giant letters spelling out "BELIEVE." Believe me, this was an utter waste of time —even the live music was shit!

Clark, me, and his friends found a place to sit and tried to figure out what we wanted to do next. Adam tried to get us to talk about pop culture or anything in the news that lacked neurons.

It wasn't until a bunch of older women holding large, quilted blankets with sayings on them sat next to us, cracking jokes at each others' expense.

My kind of people!

"Did you make those?" I asked.

The group of women perked up and turned toward us. "Yes, we did!" one of them said.

"Awesome, do you mind if we get a picture with you all and the quilts?" I asked. They weren't vagina hats, but they'd do.

As soon as the picture was taken, we thanked the ladies and headed to lunch before meeting up with my friends to start the wine walk.

23. WALK IN A MARCH

21

Timeline of Clark: Part II

JANUARY 19TH

After the women's march, we headed to lunch with Clark's friends who were still very uninteresting, even as one of them asked who my Queen B was. Lame. Adam and James left, and we met up with Serena, who attended the wine walk with us along with a couple more of Clark's insecure friends. After our walk, we headed back to the hotel and had atrocious sex. An hour later, we got to talking—a few wine glasses deep—and I spilled a truth that contradicted one of my lies. Shit! Clark began to question me. I came up with more lies to cover that truth. It'd have to do; I couldn't fuck up the assignment.

JANUARY 20TH

Things have become weird as he's a bit more cautious with me. Packing up, we checked out of the hotel to meet up with, yet again, his damn friends at PJ's. As we bowled, one of his friends threws shade to distract me—but it didn't work. We headed back to their house to watch some stupid movie about a Fire Island scam. After, we got frozen yogurt and then Clark and I parted ways.

JANUARY 24TH

Clark told me he searched for my name in the public records of the college I'm attending only to find that nothing comes up.[82] The tone of his voice suggested he's concerned about the relationship. I assured him the relationship is not over and I exposed all the lies I told, as it was time to break the trust. The downfall of the relationship began.

FEBRUARY 1ST

His family puts on a surprise birthday party for his cousin who is turning forty. I begin with fake insecurities only to be told, "Either you can come or not, but you're not going to ruin the fun I'm about to have fun tonight." That statement showed me he is no longer committed to the relationship. Later that night at the party, I quickly learned about motion-activated flushing as I molested the toilet while trying to find the handle. Now I know. His cousin became a messy drunk and cried over a deceased sister who didn't make it to forty.

---

[82] I used a different name.

22

Namaslay

"Don't fuck it up!" was all that I repeatedly thought about as Clark and I headed up the narrow wooden stairs leading to the yoga studio. Inside, peaceful ambiance filled the dimly lit common area. Clark veered to left to remove his socks and shoes and placed them into an empty cubby. I did the same.

We both headed into a brightly lit room, where fifteen other people—all sitting on their mats—chatted while waiting for the class to start. A few of the women in the front saw Clark and myself walk in and they made room for us—directly in front of the instructor's mat.

"Shit, whoever is leading the class is going to be filled with tremendous disappointment!" I said to myself.

Sitting with my legs crossed and waiting nervously, the

instructor—a middle aged women with a large Hindu tattoo stretched across her left shoulder—weaved through the crowd to her mat, greeting everyone along the way.

"Welcome everyone," she said. "Thank you so much for attending, there's a lot of you today! Let's get started."

First having everyone stand, she instructed us to do neck rolls—going one direction and then in reverse.

"Now, I want everyone to position themselves in downward dog, bending your waist and stretching out your toes," she calmly instructed.

What the fuck is downward dog? I know doggy style, but that's the extent of my yoga knowledge. Looking around room and at Clark, everyone bent over, placing their hands on the mat while arching their backs and balancing on tippy-toes.

Thinking this would land me a trip to the hospital or chiropractor, I followed suit and found myself with my ass in the air and on my tippy-toes.

"Taking in a few breaths, relax your back and if you can, pull your chin in to your chest as much as you can," the instructed added.

Closing my eyes, I took in deeper breaths, fillings my lungs as much as I could.

"Remember, exhale all the air out of your lungs. Keep exhaling out until all the old air is gone," she said.

I'm going to pass out or worse, be killed by intense positions.

• • • • •

Ten minutes before the session ended, I was completely drenched in sweat and sore. But I was proud of myself for keeping up with everyone and the many, many, many positions this activity offered. I felt like Gumby, and was more flexible than before. The yoga instructor sat down on her mat—legs crossed—and invited everyone to join her in that very pose.

"This better be easy or I'm out!" I said to myself.

Sitting down on my wet green mat, I mimicked her.

"Now, before we end the session, let's induce the spiritual sound of OM. This helps embody the divine energies of creation, preservation, and liberation."

You have to be kidding me?

I thought that was only done in the movies. Before I could finish my thought...

"OMMMMMMMMMMMMMMMMMMMMMMMM-MM....."

She's really doing this!

Everyone around me closed their eyes and hummed the chant—including Clark.

Fuck it! "OMMMMMMMMMMMMMMMMMMMM-MM..."

Peeking, I saw everybody sat with straight backs and were really focused on the chant. I couldn't help but laugh after this point. What exactly was this suppose to do? We could have spent this time in downward dog pose being lazy. Hell, I could have used the extra minutes doing nothing while my body recovered—the gym cannot compare.

The chant faded slowly and the instructor thanked everybody for joining her today.

"What did you think?" Clark asked.

"It was interesting, to say the least," I replied.

Clark smirked as he rolled up his mat.

"I'm starving, let's get some breakfast. All this intense bending and stretching as worked me up an appetite," I suggested.

As Clark and I headed to Peg's, I vowed to never do yoga again.

~~19. YOGA~~

23

Timeline of Clark: Part III

FEBRUARY 12TH

Clark and I have unprotected sex downstairs in his make -shift bedroom while his grandma is upstairs. Here's the best word to describe our sexual encounter: terrible. "Didn't have time as it was just a quickie," he told me.

FEBRUARY 13TH

Sends me nudes to inspire me while jerking off. Questioned him about the nudes and stated he took them the night before but was insecure about sending them—now he was lying to me.

FEBRUARY 14TH

Valentine's day. Clark suggest we go simple (which means cheap) because he didn't want to go extravagant. He was no longer invested in the relationship, but merely waited for it to end. I could care less. We have dinner at some low-end Chinese restaurant located in a casino, followed by arcade games where he won me a glittery dolphin. He got drunk and I remained sober. At the end of the night, we found ourselves at a bar where he suggested doing karaoke at the same place we first met. I know what he's doing. The mutual sex partner will be there (naturally) and it's a way for him to confront me about the lie I told him. Sneaky. I ask him why and then quickly changed his mind, no longer wanting to go. The days are numbered in this relationship. Thank god!

FEBRUARY 15TH

Another fucking night of him and I with his friends watching the newest episode of RuPaul's Drag Race and this time I met more of his friends—dear god! This is the also night I needed to end things with Clark and force him to break up with me—I can't take it anymore. I get drunk, but only to pretend to be wasted. I caused myself to vomit on myself, but I nailed his friend's floor as well.[83] I fake cried, causing a ruckus about our relationship, only to pretend pass out.

FEBRUARY 16TH

After waking up, I had sex with him yet again without a condom and he climaxed on me instead of inside me; a

---

[83]Deserve an Oscar for this performance.

clearcut sign I wasn't his boyfriend anymore but just some-one he has sex with. Clark asked about my ex and what happened. He wondered about how I became undetectable. I fed him some bullshit story.[84] Furious at my response, we left his friend's house after spending the night and head ed-back to his place. The car ride was tense. Later that day, he broke up with me.

It's over—THANK FUCKING GOD!

Time to write the article and get paid $500 for the hell I've been through.

---

[84]This is an assignment, he doesn't need to know the truth—as for you readers, the truth will be told at a later time.

February 18, 2019

Dear August,

Easy come, easy go—Clark broke it off. Finally! I have to say that was the hardest assignment I've ever had to endure.

Let me fill you in—cliff notes version.

I had a gut feeling about a week prior that it would end soon. He sent me a headless nude photo of himself (with a boner). Asking when he took the photo, he responded with, *"I took it last night."* His response raised a huge red flag. I followed up with another question, asking why he didn't send it to me when he took it and why was his head cut out of the

picture. His response: *"I was self-conscious about my body and my hair was just terrible."* Another red flag, as we've had sex and I've seen his hair completely messy. So, I posed the question: Are you talking to anyone else? *"It's been me and you from the start,"* he replied. Clark just lied to me.

Clark is the type of guy who doesn't know how to be in a relationship no matter how hard he tries to convince himself. My friends from my *swipe party* came over and placed bets on how long it would take for Clark to create a Grindr profile.[85]

Brian won the bet; Clark had created an account that same day, post-breakup. I texted him, accepting the fact that it was really over, as instructed by Brian. Attached is a screenshot of our mini-conversation.[86]

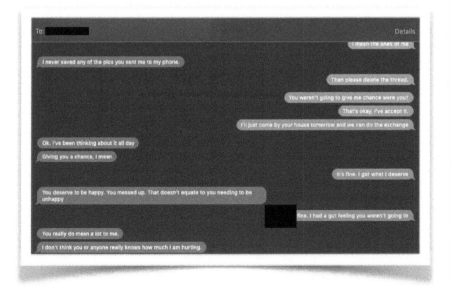

What we all found to be hilarious was the part about him **"hurting."** Little did he know that one of Brian's friend was

---

[85] Mind you, that photo he used is one that he sent to me a while back.

[86] I was still undercover for my article.

at the same club reporting back about everything he was doing including interacting with him. If you're hurting that bad, you don't go out to the club nor do you download a hookup app literally 24 hours after ending it. The only thing that was left was to give back our stuff—a clean break instead of dragging it out any further.

Clark is a twenty-seven-year-old kid who should never date and stick to what he knows best—along with the majority of the gays: sleeping around and being deceitful. The difference between Clark and myself is that he slept with that mutual sex partner (who is also a terrible in bed) because he was a drunk whore, whereas myself only slept with the same man for article purposes—journalism.

He also needs to work on building his own confidence as he was a constant poster child of insecurities. He shouldn't rely on other people to make him feel better about himself.

Always,

Allister

P.S. A guy can only take so much RuPaul, Ariana Grande, and other dumb shit with his friends. I can understand why his ex cheated on him or why he's been single for most of his life—might want to keep that fisting story to himself.

Clark has nothing to offer. Plus, his mother would be turning in her grave if she knew the type of guy he's become.

Okay, I'm done.

To: *Allister_at_home*
From: *B***EF***R_at_Work*
Subject: *Great Work*

February 20, 2019

Allister,

Upon reviewing your article, I am totally blown away by how you obtained the information to write this. Most of our writers have a hard time with it. Nonetheless, it's better than expected and will be publishing this in the following month.

I will let you know when it goes live. Looking forward to using your services again. Look for your payment in the next few days. If it doesn't deposit, please let us know!

Thanks,

Rebekah

18. GET PUBLISHED BY A WELL KNOWN PUBLICATION

24

A Company
Car Quickie

"This is going to be a quick quickie," the nervous guy I met from Grindr said.[87]

Chuckling, we found a parking spot deep within the confines of suburbia where the streetlights didn't reach.[88] Promptly, my hookup jumped the console and headed to the back where the third row of seats had already been folded down.

Efficient.

Placing my phone and keys in his cup holder, I hopped the console while trying not to step on all the empty water

---

[87] Yes, I am on Grindr at the moment and I don't care anymore—judge away.

[88] Why does that sound like something Shel Silverstein would write?

bottles that were scattered all over the place. The guy ripped off his bright yellow shorts, revealing his already erected seven.

This guy wasn't kidding when he said this would be a quick quickie.

Doing the same, I told him to lay down so I could get comfortable with what I was about to encounter. Attempting to lock lips with him, he turned his head to the side and I met his cheek instead.

"Kissing is a no, I take it?" I asked.

"It's a bit personal for me, but I'm not opposed to it," he answered.

That was a plain "no" in subtext form if I ever heard one.

What is it with gays nowadays who avoid kissing? At this point, I think we're passed personable. Pulling back, I focused past him, no longer making any sort of eye contact and figured the quicker we get this quickie done, the sooner I could head home.

"God, you're teasing me!" he announced.

"Sorry," I apologized.

"No, no it's hot!"

At least one of us was enjoying the transaction. I, on the other hand, checked out mentally after the rejected kiss.

"Lay down," he said, shifting us and nearly slamming my head against the back of the SUV.[89]

This guy had no idea about what he was doing or how

---

[89] Where do you draw the line between, "I need this type of fun in my life," and "I'm getting too fucking old for this?"

to transition smoothly between positions. This is exactly why I've abandoned all hope for random hook-ups because it only works when you're drunk.

"How does that feel?" he asked.

"So good," I exaggerated.

In a matter of minutes, the dirty deed was over and I left feeling unsatisfied. Mr. Quickie took a couple of deep breaths and placed his hand on the back window to hold himself up. He acted as though we just spent an hour sharing a hardcore sex session—he didn't even stick it in all the way.

I pushed him off me so we could pull up our pants, then climbed back to the front seat and waitedfor him to drive me back to my car.

This had been a complete waste of my time.

Is that what was to be expected from twenty-seven year olds? Clark is in the same age group and I thought maybe he was inexperienced[90]—apparently, that age group lacks sex skills.

"Sorry, my boyfriend broke it off with me," Mr. Quickie said.

Poor guy, that explained the no kissing. He's still very much in love with his ex.

"If you don't mind me asking, why did you guys breakup?"

"He went back into the closet," he hesitantly said.

My breakup with Clark didn't quite compare as it wasn't

---

[90] Clark has a lot to learn. He may have a degree in biology, but failed in sex. I guess when you're overweight and have a huge scar lining your waist from getting excess skin removed, well, I'd avoid getting naked with other people, too.

real, but here we have a guy head over heels for another who was told, "Sorry, no more gay relationship."

Rough.

As he drove up to my car and came to a stop, I looked over at the broken man and gave him a hug. At that moment, he let go of his suppressed feelings and cried into my shoulder. I knew it was what Mr. Quickie needed.

And when he finished crying, I climbed out of his company car and into mine, and we went our separate ways.

February 28, 2019

Cher Clark,

Rencontrer avec toi était très intéressant, c'est le moins qu'on puisse dire. Je n'ai jamais rencontré quelqu'un qui fasse ce qu'il faut pour être le centre de l'attention ou même quelqu'un qui tourne littéralement autour de la course de dragsters de Rupaul vingt-quatre heures sur vingt-quatre.

Pendant notre temps ensemble, vous avez beaucoup à travailler. Puis-je suggérer de ne pas dire aux gens que vous êtes un bon menteur - cela soulève tant de drapeaux rouges. Vous avez presque dit que vous ne pouviez pas être des menteurs, quelque chose que votre passé vous a fait subir - et pourtant, vous êtes amis avec quelqu'un qui a menti à sa femme pour ne pas être gay. Hypocrite? Je le pense.

Vous vous inquiétez de ce que les autres pensent de vous, oubliez ce qui compte le plus. Un véritable état d'esprit de quelqu'un qui n'a pas fini le lycée. Face à cela, vous n'appartenez pas à une relation car vous ne savez pas comment en être une. Ce que vous savez, c'est comment baiser, boire et faire la fête. Ne peignez pas les roses en rouge ici, traduction, ne soyez pas quelque chose que vous n'êtes pas.
Un jour, un gars entrera dans votre vie et vous brisera le

cœur en vous aidant à réaliser à quel point vous êtes fragile. En outre, travaillez sur votre performance au lit - ça craint. Jamais de ma vie je n'ai eu besoin de le simuler.

Vous avez peut-être pensé que vous aviez toujours deux longueurs d'avance, alors qu'en réalité, vous aviez vingt pas en arrière. Vous avez beaucoup à apprendre sur la vie cosmpolitaine.

Grandir.

La vie ne se résume pas à la boisson, au sexe, à la fête, à Ariana Grande et à RuPaul.

Celui que vous avez laissé partir,

Allister[91]

7. LEARN FRENCH

---

[91] How's that for french?

122

The "I Don't Care" Thirty Attitude

Is this what it feels like? Did I just go through pubethirty? To not care about the smallest of things such as keeping up with social media? The latest trends that populate its posts? Documenting every fucking moment of my life in fear of missing out? (Actually, that may be due to the hippest place to eat opening around the corner.) Yes, I don't care anymore. I really can't stand the drama of individuals in said relationships or the people I that I've come to know, including their opinions or judgmental thoughts.

The subtext of it all is simple, I DON'T CARE!

Jake Dupree—aka Glitter Fantasy—spoke nothing but the truth after we had a rather vibrant conversation over the phone. Jake said, "I'm going to do what I want, whatever makes me happy, and those who cannot fathom my decisions can see themselves out the door." Amen, sister—and he's doing exactly that!

You're probably asking yourself, "How does one not care anymore?" I've noticed that my phone isn't molded to my hand anymore. In the mornings, checking my phone isn't the first activity that starts my day. I leave my phone in my bedroom and when a notification goes off, I'm don't rush to check it. My logic these days is this: "if it's very important, they'll call me." Or "someone better be dead, dying, bleeding!"

What I'm also finding is that staying home is a lot more fun than getting ready and heading out for the evening. Don't get wrong, every once and a while it's necessary to hit up a restaurant or a bar to change up the scenery. But, who wants to pay for overpriced drinks? Hell to the no! A fifteen-dollar boxed wine does more justice than paying for two small sex on the beach drinks equaling the same amount. Priorities, it's all about *my* priorities. Other people can throw their dollar bills at the bartender.

I'm not sure why I didn't have this awakening earlier in the year, but like my girls say—including myself—everything happens for a reason.

Always,

Allister

To: *B_at_home*
From: *Allister_at_home*
Subject: *Embarrassed, pathetic, dumb, and yet, not surprised*

March 13, 2019

Dear B,

I still cannot believe we didn't have a proper goodbye. There were no margaritas, no wine, nor alcohol of any kind! Sending you off to your new adventure hungover is good luck, you know? Any-who...

So, I did something rather bold. I reached out to a family member of an ex. The reason: I didn't have any contact info! I realized I shouldn't have let go of this guy.

The message:

"I'm not sure if you remember me or not? I know this is out of nowhere, but I was with Derek for a long time and ended things with him for various reasons. It's been a couple of years and I haven't stopped thinking about him. I'm not sure if he's still in Reno or not, but I have no other way of contacting him, so I figured I reach out to you. It's a long shot for me to do this. I miss Derek tremendously as I shouldn't have let him go. I realized that he was perfect for me in everything I wanted. I was dumb and didn't see it before. I hope you could reach out to him and see if he would be open to reconnecting. Here is my phone number +1775*******. Like I said, it's a long shot for me to do this and don't expect him to even want to talk to me. But, I haven't stopped loving him."

The reply:
"He has a boyfriend and is happy. Sorry. He's moved on."

Feetings of being pathetic and embarrassment set in and the boldness I exerted was kicked out of the picture. I'm not surprised he already has someone in his life. I only wish that I was that person, the person he calls boyfriend. Hopefully, the podcast, the painting/wine class I signed up for, and the audition helps me forget this dumb thing I did. Change of subject, what's Colorado like?

Maybe by the time I get my ass out to see you, I'll somewhat be a rock climbing pro, at least decent enough get more than a couple feet off the ground.

Always,

Allister

P.S.

By the way, one of my all time favorite authors (and idols) just followed me on instagram. Forget meeting a celebrity in person, mine just followed me for no reason! Geeking out right now. So, I'm crossing that off my list.

> **○ INSTAGRAM**   1m ago
> [allisterdean]: Jen Lancaster (jennsylvania) started following you.

I'm totally freaking out right now!

27. MEET A CELEBRITY

To: *Allister_at_home*
From: *B_at_home*
Subject: Re: *Embarrassed, pathetic, dumb, and yet, not surprised*

March 14, 2019

Hey Allister!

Not dumb at all that you did that. Very brave actually. Most people don't have near the guts you do to do something like that. I'm proud of you for reaching out. Even receiving that cold, short, and impersonal response is better than never knowing. Who's to know if that relationship will last forever anyway? It may, but it may not.

At least you reached out. Perhaps you will receive a warmer response one day.

I do wish we could have had a proper goodbye, but maybe that means it's not actually goodbye—so that's a good thing. There's a direct flight from Reno to Denver, I'm sure. You are always welcome. Might be best if I get just a little more settled in so that I know how to be a tour guide here. Ha! I'm still learning the area. I will send you pics. It's beautiful!

Colorado.

So far it's AMAZING! I met a someone—a good guy with a good heart. He is sooo Colorado, with the beard and scruffy long hair. We hike on our dates. But he is originally from Texas, and he has that Texas drawl. Kind of a mix of Matthew McConaughey and Dr Phil; when he says, "Right," it sounds like the word "white" with about three syllables in it. 😂 Hahahaha!

He's a teacher, and even looks like one. But I cannot say it enough, he's so caring and makes me smile. I'm at his place now and must go but will definitely fill you in some more. By the way, right on about your favorite author following you!

B.

25

Poor Unfortunate Souls

TheatreWorks of NN
announces auditions for
The Little Mermaid
Directed by: J.H.

Auditions will be from 5pm - 8pm
318 Spoken Dr.
Your time slot is at—5:45pm

We are excited to use our new space
for auditions and show.

Their *new* space was in the middle of the dumpiest part

of town! Looking at the neighborhood, I reached over and quickly locked my car doors. For all I knew, someone could be hiding behind something, ready to jump out and try to steal my car.

"You've arrived! Your destination is on the right, 318 Spoken Drive," Siri confirmed.

"And you're in a sketchy part of town,[92]" I added in a British accent.

Pulling into a parking space, I wondered if I was even at the right place. As I prepared to call the number attached to the email, a bunch of people holding headshots walked by, talking up a storm about what parts they were auditioning for. Getting out and following them, I walked into a theater that appeared to be in mid-paint job because the place reeked of new paint.

Two women sat a table and called people up when the previous actor finished grabbing applications, heard them sing, and watched them perform their minute-long mono-logue while taking notes the entire time.

If I wasn't nervous before, I sure as fuck was now.

Around the corner from the front entrance, I grabbed an application, schedule, and agreement from another ta-ble.[93] Filling out the forms, I smirked at the section that asked if I had done previous stage work. I wondered if me being forced by my second grade teacher to be a cleaning elf for my class play counted.

---

[92] This usually doesn't end well in this type of neighborhood.

[93] In which a $25 dollar costume was assessed if you were chosen. If I'm paying for any type of costume...I'm keeping it. Mark my words....I'll leave with it on once the final performance is over...that's if I get a part.

I wrote "VIRGIN!" in big, bold letters for that section. I was almost going to add "go easy, it's my first time," but deemed that would cross a line.

Waiting for the current audition to finish up, I noticed the room was filled with teenagers accompanied by their parents who were much more worried about their child getting part than the actual child. I've now entered the *Twilight Zone's* episode of Dancing Moms.

"Did you gargle with salt water before we came, Tiffany?" one mom asked.

"Straighten out your back when you're up there," another instructed her child.

The dads who attended[94] were in the back tending to crying babies while giving off the vibe of *just shoot me now*. Feeling somewhat bad for them, I soon got over it as they were the ones who said "I do" to the women who lived vicariously through their spawn.[95]

Your bad, Boo Boo.

"If anyone has applications to turn in, please do it now," one of the two women announced.

Rushing up, I handed mine over and turned around before they...

"Allister, don't be shy. Show us what you've got," the one with my paperwork said.

Damn it.

---

[94] More so dragged into.

[95] Please note that when I do have a kid of my own in the future, I'll never be this type of parent. I will be dropping them off and hitting the bar. If the kid wants me to stay, I'm bringing the bar with me and will keep a bottle of wine or cosmopolitan fixings in a tote bag while enduring mediocre acting.

Being next was what I was trying to avoid. Well, I'm here—so it's now or later. Turning around, I placed my phone, keys, and wallet on their table as the woman to my left appeared horrified that I just used her thirty-dollar folded table you could find at Office Depot.

"All right, before I begin, I want to say that I do apologize for my terrible acting skills and my nails on a chalkboard signing," I told them.

All the attention was now on me. Not only were the two women completely focused on my soon-to-be not even runner-up Oscar or Grammy performance, but all the other *auditionees* stopped what they were doing to watch me.

FUCK!

"Just as I practiced a million times in front of the mirror," I told myself.

And boom, I went into Ursula's monologue,[96] mimicking Miss Octopus' movements and tone of voice. The women both had the beginnings of a smile, which was a very good sign. Transitioning from speech to song, the room filled with reverbs of my so-called singing.

A few beads of sweat dripped down my forehead. Is this how all great actors and actresses felt before stardom? And just like that, my song was over.

Staring at them, we all shared am awkward moment of silence.[97] Walking up to the table, I grabbed my belongings.

Was it that bad? Were there no words that could be formed?

---

[96] It's the scene where Ariel meets Ursula in her cave...you know that conversation they have before the song.

[97] Probably for the death of acting/singing career.

"And you sure you haven't auditioned before?" one of them asked.

"It says virgin on my paperwork," I said, pointing to my bold handwriting.

"Well, I was impressed," the other said.

I was confused. Did they just not hear me singing or were they both in LA LA Land during my "song?"

"Thank you for auditioning. Expect an email for the casting list."

"Okay, thank you," I said, then walked away.

That was that.

~~15. AUDITION FOR A PLAY~~

To: *Allister_at_home*
From: *TWNN_at_work*
Subject: *Artown 2019: The Little Mermaid Cast Announced!*

March 20, 2019

Hello all!

First of all, let us say that this decision was extremely difficult because of the immense talent that we were so honored to have audition!

We are thrilled to announce the cast of the *The Little Mermaid*. See you all at the first Read-Through on April 1st, at 7:30p.m. at our new home.

We are scheduled to do eighteen shows: Artown, Tahoe, and at a major theater[98] here in town.

So, with that said...we're excited! This is our largest production yet!

There will be another email of scheduled rehearsal dates and times. If you have any questions in the meantime, please feel free to reach out!

---

[98] This is bigger than I realized! I'm singing in front of all these people....no pressure there.

We look forward to working with you all soon!

———

Allister Dean — Prince Eric[99]

Till then,

TWNN

---

[99] Shut. The. Fuck. Up!

26

Girl, Let Me Tell You About My Week

"Are you available to record right now!?" Alex texted.

"Yes, I am girl!" I responded.

"Great! Bring wine of your liking. See you in an hour!" she said.

After a quick shower, a Merlot purchase, and twenty-minute drive, I arrived at Alex's front doorstep ready to record a podcast episode for *The Hate Journals*.

"Allister!" Alex excitedly yelled, "Come in, come in!"

"Thanks for having me over, this is going to be a real treat!" I said, walking inside.

Handing her the bottle of Merlot, Alex quickly introduced her, *you can tell I workout*, hockey-watching hus-band[100] before heading upstairs to a nook of a room record-ing studio where another one of the girls of the podcast was waiting.

"Hi! I'm AP," she said, proffering her hand.

"Nice to meet you, I'm Allister," I said, shaking her hand.

"Soooooooooo glad you could fill in for Britt on such short notice."

"It's my pleasure, I really was just sit-ting at home doing nothing," I said.[101]

"Before we get started, I need a cigarette," Alex confessed.

"Me too. Do you smoke?" AP asked.

"Nah, but this is a great time for us to talk," I suggested.

"Agreed!" Alex said, leading the way to the backyard.

• • • • •

Ten minutes into recording and into my second glass

---

[100] Total sweetheart!

[101] I really was doing nothing at home and that, my friends, is a dangerous thing.

of wine, Alex jumped over to me and asked how my week was going.

"Girl, let me tell you," I said, adjusting my seat,[102] "First off, I auditioned for *The Little Mermaid* and was casted as Prince Eric!"

Alex and AP cheered my accomplishment.

"So, Thursday I was invited to hangout with a hot, straight buddy of mine[103] and couple of his friends at the *The Eddy*—which is an outside bar filled with fun activities. Botchy ball, huge Jenga, and stuff like that. We set a time for 3 p.m. and he said he would call me when he was heading out—mind you this was at noon," I told the girls, who were completely focused on my story.

"2:30 hit and no phone call—that's when I decided to call him and told me, 'Hey, my car battery died and I'm on the other side of town.' Before I go any further, let me tell you that he's a full-time nurse but also restores cars and sells them on the side, along with investing in stock. Any who, I told him I would drive out to where he was and help out."

"That was nice of you to do," AP said.

"Is he hot?" Alex bluntly asked.

"Like ridiculously hot! I want to sleep with him," I sexually said.

"Oh girl!" Alex said in a Georgia accent while waving fanning her face with her hand.

"After all was said and done, we headed to his friend

---

[102] And also pausing for dramatic effect.

[103] Straight and absolutely curious.

Kendra's apartment to pick her up. I stepped inside and I was utterly shocked."

"Why? Was it dirty?" Alex said.

"The complete opposite my dear, Ii was like stepping into one of her *Pinterest* boards, I swear to God! Everything was placed a certain way, like the lighting was fucking ideal. *Better Homes and Gardens* magazine would be at your front door step ready to photograph this apartment." I said.

"Were you thrown because you walked into an ascetically pleasing apartment?" AP asked, sliding into the conversation.

"No I wasn't, the only thing that came to mind was *James Charles Fake-Ass Bitch!*" I said.

The room filled with laughter after I said that. But, a slight worry came over me: had I gone too far about my thoughts?

"Then she asked if what she was wearing was appropriate for *The Eddy*. Kendra was wearing a white, long-sleeved crop top which I thought was great, but her tiny grey booty shorts screamed *give me a cardboard sign because I'm homeless.* I said no on the shorts to her. After that, we took vodka shots and headed to our destination, only spending an hour there just be back at her apartment where Shawn's car died right as he pulled in, blocking everyone else in," I said.

The girls looked over at me, sitting on the edge of their seats, eager to know what the hell happened next.[104]

"This is where it gets interesting, ladies. Did you know that when a BMW's battery dies the car is useless? Like, you

---

[104] Does this not happen to anyone else!

cannot put it into neutral and push it out of the way. It's stationary."

"All right with that said, do not email us on how to fix BMWs as we do not need that and do not care!" Alex interjected with a laugh.

"So, he sent Kendra to fetch tools. Meanwhile, the night lingered on, and a gentleman who lived in the complex who needed to leave to pick up his girlfriend couldn't because he was blocked in. My sexy hot friend began to call this man names, causing the stranger to call the police. Wrapping this story up, by the time Kendra came back the police had arrived. Kendra suggested that I should go home."

"Noooooooooooo," AP and Alex both say.

"Yes, so I did. I got into my car and left." I added.

"Wow!" Alex says.

"That's how my week went," I said, laughing.

AP and Alex laughed. They may think that my life is a bit crazy from what I just told them, but, that was just a normal day for me.

16. BE A GUEST ON A PODCAST

27

Camping(ish)

A last minute, on the spot decision has just been made.

Sitting deep inside my closet is untouched camping equipment (tent and sleeping bag)[105] that's slowly collecting dust. Now, all of last year I commented, blubbered, and swore to many, many that people I'd go camping—that I'd really get out there and rough it in the wilderness.

There's only one problem: I'm not a camping guru nor do I know where one goes to "rough it".[106]

Backyard it is!

I figured, what better place is here to test out the

---

105 A Christmas gift from the parents.

106 And you thought this gay was just all about shopping and latte's—yes, I just realized how broad that generalization was. In my defense, once someone gets to know me they have a certain perspective. That's about to change.

equipment before hand than a controlled environment versus traveling to a questionable, remote area and nearly killing myself for a lack of camping knowledge?[107]

Smart.

In the kitchen, I read over the 8.5 x 11 double-sided paper of instructions (that barely incorporated pictures for reference). Everything started to click instantly.[108]

"Is it that easy?" I wondered, staring at the pieces scattered across the floor.

Scooping up all the pieces and carrying them out to the backyard, I laid them out once again. I slowly connected pieces to make four long rods (the best way to describe this

is when you see a blind person using their white cane. It can collapse and resume its extended form because of the stretchy band running through the middle of all the pieces).

In minutes (and with careful instruction reading) the tent was built. I must admit, out of anything I tried for the first time, this had to be the easiest task I ever did.

It's like I was meant to be a camper!

Now in the backyard, I

---

[107] What others might think is a dangerous spot, I would think is acceptable.

[108] Ikea needs to hire the person who wrote these, seriously!

laid out my thick sleeping bag and pillow along with a lantern and a copy of Bear Grylls' book *How to Stay Alive, The Ultimate Guide For Any Situation* (life or death situations, medical emergencies, great escapes, and more). You never know what could happen in one's backyard.[109]

Scooping up Mercury and Mars, I zipped us all into the tent and we were officially camping(ish).

Now what?

It's ten at night and I'm in a sleeping bag that's in a tent staked in my backyard...and this was't very exciting. Was I missing something, or possibly doing something wrong? Everyone I know who camps expresses how much they LOVE getting out into the wilderness—is my boredom because I'm in my backyard?

Before figuring out why the camping magic wasn't presenting itself, a loud crackling sound burst out of nowhere.

"You have to be kidding me!" I exclaimed.[110]

And just like that, the sky opened up and rain fell hard against my tent. A slight breeze blew soon after. Did mother nature decide to fuck with me and say, "Hey, let's stir things up for Allister and his backyard camping(ish) experience?"

The only ones who were not affected by the sudden change in weather were the pooches. Looking down, both Mercury and Mars were sound asleep at my feet, both contented as if someone had just turned on a rainforest podcast

---

[109] Bear suggests on page 23: pack a condom. One can hold up to two liters of water and they also keep things dry since they are waterproof. Let's not forget the tampon for firelighting, but do pads work as well.

[110] I don't even know why I'm even surprised. Nevada weather is bipolar..one minute it's sunny and the next it's snowing.

to help them sleep.

Lucky little bastards.

Grabbing my eye mask,[111] I settled deeper in my sleeping bag and attempted to catch some shut eye. However, another problem presented itself: the uneven, bumpy ground that dug into my back. Is this why people bring a blow up mattress?

To my dogs, I am the blow up mattress.

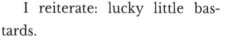

I reiterate: lucky little bastards.

Sighing, flashes of my warm cozy bed infiltrated my mind, causing me to think about saying, "Screw it," give up, and go back inside.

"No, I am sticking this out, for fucking sake!" I say to myself, "Being out here isn't so bad, a bit nippy, nonetheless not the worst."

Spoke too soon.

Crackles filled and lit up the night sky as rain fell. I had to open my mouth allowing a window of opportunity for karma (or whatever celestial being) to come and rain on my mediocre parade—the silver lining of it all is no podcast needs to be downloaded to help me sleep—or so I thought.

The rain grew heavier and heavier as the night grew on.

---

[111] Thank you FREE PEOPLE! Best money ever spent, may purchase another.

It almost felt like my tent was about to give up and rip apart. Grabbing my "wilderness" survival book, I scammed the index/table of contents for help on harsh rainstorm.

In a nutshell, Bear advised to keep calm and enjoy what nature provides during your outdoor stay. He's taking the *Four Seasons* too literally. What's next, is he going to suggest that I line my tent with tampons and pads to help soak up any water that happens to leak in my tent?

Thank Good he's pretty.

Doing such, I laid there completely awake, aware, and irradiated. Everything was honey-dorey up till now. Texting Devany about my twist of events, she couldn't help but laugh at my misery, in turn, I couldn't help it either.

How do people do this sort of thing on a regular basis? More importantly, how is this even fun?

Now, if I had a Subaru or a vehicle like it, you best believe the very back would be changed into a makeshift bed.

• • • • •

The next morning, barley getting any sleep, I was awaken by the carp sounds of the jet stream sprinklers hitting the tent harshly. Pulling the eye mask off, the pups were still fast asleep unnerved.

Lucky little bastards.

Checking the time on my phone, it was five-in-the-morning.

Sighing, I've only been a sleep for two hours. I need my eight hours, any less and the kraken emerges.

Waiting fifteen minutes for the sprinkler to finish its cycle, I gathered the pups and headed back inside my house to where warmth and coffee could be found—followed by a hot shower to wash off any nature that attached itself from last night.

Is this what true camping is? If it is, I better have a bottle or two or four of merlot packed away in case of emergencies to help get me through the night or couple of days of sheer wilderness.

Bear can eat his heart out if you're not living with all the essentials.

~~22. CAMPING~~

March 29, 2019

Hey B,

While you're living life and enjoying the beautiful landscape of Colorado, I'm enjoying a rather unusual view of the house across the way on the other side of Marrowleaf Way. The house has been vacant and untouched since the people who rented it out moved months ago—which I have to say has been rather peaceful (there are no more rowdy, unruly children running around.)

Part of my morning ritual includes gazing out my kitchen window to watch the world play out before me while Mr. Coffee makes my *wake me the fuck up* juice. Opening said blinds this morning, the once vacant house was not vacant. Two differently aged men were unloading movie lights and what appeared to be camera equipment from their creepy, white, child-kidnapping van. Mind you, I did write down their plate number just in case.

Ten minutes later, the two men had set up the lights outside a couple of windows, turned them on, and repositioned them for what they needed. Next, they placed cameras inside and two more people arrived and entered the house.

Texting a good friend—Devany, I asked what the strange occurrence could be.

"They could be photographing the house to sell it better on the market?"

This wasn't a million-dollar mansion or Kim Kardashian-West's summer get-a-way that *Better Homes* magazine wanted to feature!

No, the more I carefully watched what was going on, the more I noticed small details that I first missed. For one—the windows were lit form the outside, the blinds were closed, and of the people who arrived later, the woman was a busty blonde and the gent was a gym rat.

They're filming a damn porno!

Almost felt like I just won a round of CLUE—he did her, with his penis, in the house, probably everywhere. Replying back to Devany with my well-thought accusation, she asked, "What kind of porno is being filmed?" I wasn't about to waltz my happy ass over there and spy through the blocked windows. Plus, I didn't need to be kidnapped and thrown in their creepy white van.

Always,

Allister

To: *Allister_at_home*
From: *Mitch_at_home*
Subject: *Guilt Is Killing Me*

March 30, 2019

Dear Allister,

The last time we spoke, you were apologizing about how our relationship ended because of you, but still to this day, it's not all on you. It takes two to tango. I'm as much at fault for not communicating when issues arose.

That's not the reason I'm reaching out, however. I'm not sure if you're still friends with Serena, but a week after things ended she reached to me and disclosed all you said about me.[112] Honestly, I'm not mad about it—hell, I vented to my friends as well.

Just thought that since you reached out with an apology (which is amazing and very bold), I should be a good guy, too and warn you about the actions of this so-called friend of yours.

Mitch

---

[112] WTF! That bitch!

To: *Serena_at_home*
From: *Allister_at_home*
Subject: *No Longer Welcome In My Life*

March 30, 2019

Backstabber,[113]

It's amazing to me how a friendship of ten years means nothing to you!

After speaking with an ex last night who felt the need to come clean, I found out that you deliberately went out of your way to message him and spill all the vented, negative comments I made about him after my relationship with him ended terribly. And this, just before our friendship, a week later, went south over me not attending to your bachelorette party.

What I don't find surprising about all of this is that another ex, months prior, mentioned a comment I made about him that I only shared with you.

Why the fuck would you do that?

So, not only are you a terrible friend/person, you're a liar at

---

[113] Shit is about to hit the fan!

best.[114] And for that, you are no longer welcome in my life. Second chances are something I normally don't do, but it was a huge mistake giving you one.

The gays at the club are right—you'e spiraling.

Have a nice life.

Allister

---

[114] Cheating on your husband, consistent lying to your friends...you're on an amazing streak.

28

I Have To Pay?
Don't Touch Me!
Well, Then.

"Come grab a script," the director said with smile, opening a large box filled with freshly printed text.

Forty kids (ages ranging from three to sixteen) jumped to their feet and raced to obtain a script. I, on other hand, remained in my seat, not looking to get trampled just to get a copy.

While waiting for the mob scene to dwindle, I noticed there were only three adults, besides the TWNN crew, who were part of the production. That meant one of these teenage (underage) girls was cast as Ariel.

Worried, I walked up to the director with a couple of

questions.

"Hey, do I need to shave my beard just a tad?" I asked while being handed a script, "The reason I'm asking is because I do look older and it would appear Ariel, whoever she maybe, would authentically look sixteen. I don't want to give off that daddy-issue vibe."

The director laughed, "Totally get what you're saying. Maybe shave a little bit off."

Flashing a nervous smile, I nodded and headed back to my seat.

Before opening the first page, a girl (who thinks she's funny) turned around and asked who I was and what part I was playing.

"I'm Allister and I'm playing the part of Prince Eric."

"Oh dang, he's cute!" someone yelled.[115]

Shaking my head, I continued to look over the script. I noticed that not only was I in the very first scene, but it was a singing part, too.

Just my luck.

"Looks like everyone got a script," the director said, surveying the room, "Perfect. Before we start the first read-through, there's a couple of

---

[115] Okay, let's pray an adult said that.

things I want to go over. The very last page of you script, head there please."

Doing what I'm told, I skimmed over the page to find big, bold dollar signs with attached prices—what the hell?

"There's a twenty-five dollar costume fee along with Ad Copy space that everyone needs to find a sponsor for. If you cannot find one, then you'll be paying for it," the director announced.

Wait a fucking second.

So, not only is this company looking to fill parts, but they expect the people they cast to pay for their costumes and sell space?

What kind of company was this? Isn't this what they're supposed to do before ever considering a production? I decided to see how the read-through went before allowing panic mode to set in.

•••••

"We're at the top of page 66," the director announced, "Go ahead, Prince Eric."

Nerves struck me. Reading had never been problem for me, as I read to myself all the time.[116] Besides, I'm a novice in a room full of seasoned, underage *actors*.[117]

"Allister, we're waiting on you," she said in an irritated voice.

FUCK IT!

---

[116] Mercury and Mars are growing tired of it, I'm sure. They leave any room when I start.
[117] This isn't broadway, nor are we living in L.A. So, they are not actors, just people who like to act. Don't deny my logic!

Diving right into my lines, I channeled my inner Disney Eric and gave a mediocre performance.[118]

"That was good," the director said with a smile.

Good? Or was she just being kind, afraid of hurting my feelings?

"You did really good," a twelve-year-old blonde kid said, gently placing his hand on my forearm.

"Um, thank you," I awkwardly said, moving my arm away from him.

What the hell just happened?

Was this kid really putting the moves on me, so boldly? First off, *ew* and secondly, when do we get a break so I can quickly change seats and get away from little Miss James Charles predator here?

• • • • •

"Thanks guys! The first read-through was amazing and I can already see the characters coming out—see you all next week!" the director excitedly said.

Walking hastily out the front door, a short woman with brown fried hair (who wasn't married) stepped in front of me, blocking my path.

"Hi Allister, just wanted to remind you of the ad copy space that needs to be filled. If you can't find anyone to pay for the space, then we need $75 dollars from you. This money helps pay for the set and the playbill," she informa-

---

[118] In reality, I'm a mother-fucking mermaid!

tively conveyed.[119]

"I'm sorry, and don't take this the wrong way, but who are you?" I asked.

"I apologize. I'm Emily, head of TWNN. I'm talking with everyone who is on my list about the ad space and you're next on my list," Emily said with a smile.

"Well, it's nice to meet you Emily and I'll have to get back to you on that," I said, tip-toeing my way around her toward the door.

"It's due next week," she emphasized.[120]

"Noted!"

Once out the door and in my car, I raced home, made a quick stop at *In & Out Burger* first, then whipped out my computer and did what needed to be done.

I wouldn't be caught up in this damn drama!

---

[119] Isn't that what those sponsors at the bottom of the email you sent are for?

[120] What a hustler! I wondered if she did this with the men she dated? "I need you tell me if you want to be my boyfriend by next week!" I didn't see a ring on her finger.

April 2, 2019

TWNN Council,

First and foremost, thank you for the opportunity to audition—it was an amazing experience. But after careful consideration, I'm must withdraw from *The Little Mermaid*. There are too many conflicting dates, and I'm just uncomfortable to move forward due to a lot of factors that have transpired.

I don't expect a refund on the $25 costume fee I've already donated. But as of today, I will no longer be a part of this production.

Thank you so much for your time,

Allister Dean

April 2, 2019

Allister,

I wish you all the best. Anything specific you can share about the uncomfortable factors? I am always interested in feedback to improve TWNN and cast experience. If you decide to share, feel free to give me a call directly.

Best Regards,

Lucy M.[121]

---

[121] Who the fuck is Lucy?

29

Two Drinks and A Shot Gets Me A French Kiss

After weeks of planning,[122] a couple of my girls and I decided to have drinks in support of a new local bar, *Rum Sugar Lime*.

"Isn't this place simply amazing?" I exclaimed, handing over my credit card to the muscular bartender who wore a fitted Hawaiian shirt.[123]

"How did you ever find this place?" Bev asked, wide-eyed.

---

[122] More like constant bickering of when and where to meet for damn drinks.

[123] Nice touch. I couldn't stop staring at his arms and massive pecs. I'm going to take tequila shots off of them, followed by some intense licking.

"By sheer accident, love. I was scrolling through my Facebook feed and a *Grand Opening* promotion popped up. Lucky, right?" I shared, taking the first sip of my delicious cosmopolitan.

Bev nodded with a smile.

"What do you think, Heather?" I asked.

Anytime this girl finds herself in a new place, silence overcomes her and the only way to break that is by getting her an *AMF*.[124]

After paying the bill and handing each girl their drink, we made claim at a table in the middle of the bar—the perfect spot to get noticed and hear most of the conversations happening around us.

If my nights of weekend partying at gay bars in my twenties taught me anything, it's finding the sweet spot of the establishment where it's only a step away to the dance floor, grabbing another drink, or mingling.[125]

"There are a lot of cute guys here, Allister. Maybe you can find another guy to write an article about—this time about hot, heavy sex," Bev said, giggling while flirtatiously licking her straw.

"I'm good, but you have a better chance at finding someone, for the night, especially if you keep using that straw for advertisement," I said, titty-smacking her back to PG.

"Nobody likes a whore, Bev," Heather chimed in, sipping more of her liquid courage.

---

[124] For those who are alcoholic virgins or stick to that one drink, AMF = Adios Mother Fucker. Try one...if you dare.

[125] Welcome to networking 101.

Using her selective hearing skills, Bev continued flirtatiously eye-fucking every cute guy that crossed her path.

"We've lost her," Heather commented.

"Hold on, let's make sure. Bev, what's the meaning of life?" I asked.

"What do you all think of that guy over there?" she responded.

"Yep. Lost her," I muttered.[126]

Heather giggled and sipped more of her drink, but could still see that she hurt from her most recent breakup. I had been totally rooting for her relationship to succeed—hell, I was already planning her wedding.

If Heather was having hard time finding love, there wasn't hope for the rest of us.

"Fuck!" Bev said, quickly turning around ducking her head down.

"What?" I asked, trying to figure out what just happened.

"You're not going to believe who just walked through the door?"

"I have a feeling you're going to enlightenment me, so quit with the build up and spill," I said in a bitchy tone.

"One of your ex's just walked through the door," she said. Looking past her, I saw it was someone I hadn't seen in over five years.[127]

Is it me or does it seem like most of my exes are deciding to come out the woodworks? First, it was an email from

---

[126] Dicksand is a very dangerous thing. Don't ever get caught up in it.
[127] And it's not Mr. San Diego...he's married.

Mitch about my gossiping ex-friend, and now this.

"So what?" I asked, calmly smiling to both girls, "I was bound to run into past loves[128] and right now I feel this a test on how I'm going to handle this situation and let me tell you, I'm going to handle this—him—like he's just a regular guy."

"Yeah, a regular guy you have a history with," Heather commented.

"How many of those AMFs have you drunk?" I asked, feeling cocky

"Still my first," she said, taking another sip.

"Well, you might want to slow down. I'm not ready to deal with bitchy Heather. If you'll excuse me, I'm going to use the restroom and continue with our fabulous night."[129]

Polishing off my cosmopolitan and asking Bev to order another, I casually headed to the men's room.

• • • • •

Hyperventilating in one of the bathroom stalls, I wrestled with my thoughts. "What the fuck is going on? Out of all the places tonight, my ex decided to step into this bar— besides the fact this bar just opened, but still, it's a ways away from downtown and Kevin doesn't venture outside of that area unless he's in another city."[130]

"Just have to stay calm and collected. So what if Mitch is

---

[128] More so dodging them.

[129] I really need to find a new way of saying fabulous. It's starting to date me.

[130] Dumbest life rule Kevin ever set for himself.

here and sees me all single. He came here with just his buds —far as I can tell," I said to myself.

Believing 30% of my pep talk, I opened the stall and headed to sink to wash my hands. (I still have to wash them even if I didn't do anything.) You never know who or what has recently touched any part of the bathroom.

As I wiped my hands, a cluster of drunk ex-fraternity guys (that never grew out of that Greek-life phase) entered the bathroom, loudly causing a ruckus.

"Oh, look what we have here," one of them said and stumbled toward me while looking at my reflection in the mirror, "Wanna do some coke with us?"

This is the second time now something of this nature has happened.[131] Do I have coke-head written on my forehead somewhere?

"No, thank you," I politely told him.

"Are you sure?"

"Yea, more for you bro," I said placing a hand on his shoulder.

"Yeah, okay bro," he said returning to his posse who waited for him with already made lines.[132]

Walking back to my group with a sense of confidence in my step, Bev, on the other hand, looked liked she had just committed treason on her country.

"I'm sorry Allister, I didn't want to be rude. Mitch came over and we had mini-conversation," Bev confessed.

---

[131] The first time was at a dive bar where two guys were doing lines on a toilet seat.

[132] Jesus Christ, that was fucking fast.

Heather stayed quiet and sipped her drink.[133]

"What did you guys discuss?" I asked.

"Well, Mitch asked how we both were doing and then asked if you were here."

"Great, now he knows I'm here. I need another cosmopolitan," I sighed.

Waving down the handsome barkeep, I sat down on one of the available stools and gave my drink order.

"Make that two!" I added.

"Sounds like you have a rough week?" someone to my left said.

I looked over and saw a guy in his mid-thirties wearing a bright blue polo that showed off his broad chest and large bicep/triceps. He smiled at me.

"More like my ex just walked through the door and was asking about me. I don't know what to say or even talk about or than 'hi, how are you, banging anyone?' That just doesn't work." I explained.

"Terrible conversation starter, if anything let him come to you and start the conversation," he advised. "I'm Casey, by the way."

"Allister, and you're absolutely right!" I said, shaking Casey's hand.[134]

"Which one is he?" Casey asked, scouting the room.

"He's the one near the front door in the god awful green v-neck shirt," I gestured behind me.

Casey glanced around, spotted my ex, and rolled his

---

[133] How many drinks did Heather have during my mini-meltdown in the bathroom?

[134] His grip!

eyes, "You're way better looking than him. If anything, he should be trying to win you back."

"There's no winning back anything. He and I are just not a match, I just don't want him to see how single I am," I said, sipping my cosmo.

"You're not single," Casey said, ordering another drink.

Did he just not hear what I said? I'm single as fuck!

"But I am."

"Nope—you're with me tonight," Casey said smirking.

"There's no way Mitch is not going to believe you're with me," I said.

Casey laughed and turned himself toward me.

"Let's take a shot, and if you pay for two rounds of drinks and even I'll make Hollywood believe we're together."

"Aren't you straight?" I asked, raising an eyebrow.

"Yes, but your ex doesn't need to know that. Besides, isn't it every gay man's fantasy to make out with a straight guy?" He said.

"Most, I'm sure, but I'm not a predator. But it's sex they're really after," I said.

"Well, then I don't mind helping a guy out. However, I do want to ask your blonde friend out on date," Casey said.

Pimping out my friend for the sake of upstaging an ex-boyfriend isn't something I was absolutely comfortable with, but...

"Deal!" I said, turning around. "Bev, you're going out with this guy, Casey, in the next week."

Bev looked confused to what just happened.

"What happens now?" I said, waiting for instructions.

"Now, you order me another drink and a shot of vodka, then come grab me when you're leaving. I have a feeling you're going to leave before he does," Casey said, winking at me.[135]

• • • • •

1:00 a.m.

Had to hand it to Casey, Mitch was still going strong and by the looks of it, he wasn't going anywhere.

"Hey, Heather, I'm ready to go. Are you two ready?" I asked in her ear.

She didn't say anything, but nodded due to the over-powering music obstructing any other sounds.

"I ordered an Uber, it's a blue Prius and the driver's name is Sam. Head outside and wait for it. I'll be there shortly." I said in her ear.

Back at the bar where Casey never left his stool, I placed my hand on his back getting his attention.

"The time has come I see," he said getting up out of his seat.

The man with the plan looked over in the direction of where Mitch sat. He hadn't moved from his spot, either.

"Follow my lead," Casey said, winking at me again.

He took my hand, threaded his fingers with mine, and lead me to the front door. Out of the corner of my eye, I checked to see if Mitch had been watching—he wasn't.

By the door, Casey pulled me close—as in he closed the

---

[135] Why did Casey give off the whole prostitute vibe?

gap between us, my hands on his chest, his arms wrapped around my waist, kind of close.

"Um, what are you doing?" I said to Casey.

"Getting someone's attention, which from the looks of it, he's now staring—along with a few other people with him."

Wanting to turn around and see the expressions on their faces, Casey instead leaned in a very delicately locked his lips with mine.[136] Only lasting for a full minute, Casey pulled away with a smile.

Outside, Heather gave two thumbs while Bev (from what I could tell) held up her phone and recorded the whole thing.

"All right, this is where you leave. I've slipped my phone number in your back pocket to give to your blonde friend," Casey said, loosening his grip on me.

And just like that, I went from *this is amazing* to *oh, I'm back to pimping out my friend for selfish reasons*.

Casey really knew how to kill a vibe.

Leaving, the blue Prius pulled over in front of the bar and the three of us instantly got in. In my peripheral, I could see Mitch gazing my way.

"Allister, I'll send you Mitch's reaction to you kissing that guy. Are you sure he's straight?" Bev said.

I couldn't help but laugh.

13. ~~KISS A STRAIGHT MAN~~

---

[136] It takes a very secure straight man to lock lips with another man.

61

Instagram,

What the hell are you doing, removing my sexy shirtless photos from the feeds of hashtags; #gay, #gaydaddy, #instagay, #homo, #gaybearded, #gayboy, #gaysnap, or pretty much any hashtag that has the word *gay* in it? Censorship of the male body is not applicable now-a-days.

If you're going to act on it, might I suggest doing the same for women who are in nothing but bras or bikinis. Remember what happened to Tumblr? Yea, it nearly shut down because of the content restrictions and you're heading down the same path.

People are shifting to *Twitter* to upload said shirtless pictures—*Twitter!* I have one and still, to this day, I don't understand the concept of it or even know how to use it fully, but I'm determined to keep using it!

Also, quit crashing all the time. It gets rather annoying thinking my account has been hacked, deleted, or for some damn reason won't work properly. I love seeing the red banner that says, *Could not connect / refresh.* I *instahead* to Twitter and search the hashtag #instagramdown to confirm everything is down...again.

Instagram, you instasuck! Wait, hold up, got to do this correctly—#instasuck!

Always,

Allister

To: *Lucy_at_home, Eve_at_home, Kitty_at_home*
From: *Allister_at_home*
Subject: *My New Neighbor Es Muy Caliente—I Couldn't Help It*

May 5, 2019

Ladies,

Happy Cinco De Mayo!

Endless margarita's must start at noon—if not, then make it happen.

The house next to me was recently rented out to a couple (I think they're a couple). He's a military man and boy I love catching him in his uniform when he leaves for work. She, on the other hand—I assume—some kind of medical assistant work from the scrubs she wears, but I could care less what the hell she does.

What's funny is that they never leave together for anything. Could they be siblings who are also roommates? Nonetheless, Mr. Military man has his office set up in the room across from my bedroom. He can see into mine, and I into his. In the mornings, little does he know I can see everything.

Mornings are now worth waking early for! Mr. Military man, for some reason, gets dressed in his office. I love seeing his toned body walk in, fresh out of the shower, when the wrapped towel sits just above his *area*, barely hanging on to his hips. It feels like he does it on purpose.

The other night, around 1:00 a.m., I woke up in need of some H20. Coming back from the kitchen, and just before I climbed back into bed, I caught Mr. Military man pleasuring himself with headphones on.

He forgot to shut his blinds!

And let me tell you, the man was packing! I tried to see what kind of porno he was sexually engrossed in, but the laptop was angled away from me. So, no chance for me to see which team he played for. UGH!

The guy was going at it for at least thirty minutes until the mighty climax! After that, he walked around the room bare-ass naked, cleaning himself up with whatever was available around him. I think he used a shirt.

Always,

Allister

P.S,

I'm hoping there's a round two. Maybe he'll doing something more exciting!

Mr. Robert Warren

&

Ms. Rachel Keene

Will Not Know of your
Presence the Day of Their Wedding

Saturday May Sixteenth Two Thousand Nineteen
At 12:00 Pm at The Lavender Fields

Reception Follows
Soon After

<u>Adults Only, Open Bar</u>

Dinner Menu includes:

Herb Roasted Chicken, Rice Pilaf with Apricots
Fresh Asparagus wrapped in Bacon & Rolls

Please No Gifts
We Will Have a Honeymoon
Contribution at Reception

30

Who Are You With...
Bride or Groom?

"If everybody could please rise and help me welcome Mr. and Mrs. Warren!" a man in a beige suit announced.[137]

Standing, my presence is lost in a sea of people who clap (and whistle) at the newlyweds making their way down the steps to the common area of the reception.

Purple and white, the choice colors of the ceremony, were displayed throughout with paper streamers and plastic table clothes. The (real) center piece flowers consisted of tulips and daisies added a certain cuteness to their Dollar Store ambiance.

The two waved at everyone, lightly touching shoulders

---

[137] A suit that could doubled as a going to church on Easter Sunday outfit.

of those who were close enough, as they made their way to the main table where the groomsmen and brides-maids were.

"Those poor bridesmaids—wearing those hideous dresses in that awful purple shade," I said under my breathe.

"What was that dear?" an elderly woman of 65 asked me.

"I'm sorry sweetie, I didn't say anything."

"Oh, I swear you did. Which side are you on?"

"The bride's," I said.

"How do you know her?" she asked.

Did I blow my cover already?

"Oh, we're long time friends—we go way back," I answered her.

"That's not ans....."

"Anyway, it was lovely chatting with you. I'm going to grab more champagne before they start the toasts," I said, cutting her off.

I walked to the bar, where a late twenty-something guy stood waiting for his next client. He filled out his bartending outfit quite nicely.

"Hi. Another champagne, please," I said, sliding my glass over to him.

"Be careful of her," he muttered.

"I'm sorry?"

"She's a feisty old woman. I've been watching her all night and she's grilling anyone who isn't family."

"Good to know, thank you."

"Since you're crashing this wedding, I'd steer clear," he said with a smile, sliding back my filled glass.

"What gave it away?" I asked.

"You're body language."

"How so?"

"Just know. When she asked you a question, your body language read *I don't belong here, and I'm hoping you're not going to pick up on that.*"

He was good. If he was able to read that from a far, I wonder who else did?

"I'm a terrible liar—don't take me to Vegas. I'd loose your first born son," I joked, flirting.

The bartender laughed, "Now, get back out there and have some before they kick you out."

Smirking, I headed back and went to a different table where like-minded (and close in age) individuals were getting sloshed by the minute.[138]

• • • • •

With glass number five, the best man announced the couple's first dance. As the groom led his bride from their table to the dance floor, the lights suddenly dimmed and the sounds of *White Snake—Is This Love?*, played over the

---

[138] Sloshed and won't interrogate me, perfect.

loudspeakers.[139]

"Are you going to go dance?" bartender guy asked me, shuffling around some of the bottles of wine.

"Nope, remember I need to keep a low profile and I figure this is the best place to be while all that love is out on the dance floor," I tell him. "I'm realizing, I don't even know your name?"

"It's Austin, and you are?"

"Allister," I said, downing my champagne.

"How long are you going to stay?" Austin asked.

"Probably till cake cutting time or until Grandma Twenty Questions figures out I'm a crasher," I said with chuckle.

Austin filled glass number six asking if I needed a water to balance out.

"No, I'm actually not feeling anything from this bubbly—which is odd for me, total lightweight here," I confess.[140]

Everyone clapped as the song ended and the dance floor was empty once again. Winking at Austin, I headed back to the table of twenty-something sloshes and found two girls kissing one another. Anymore rounds and the guys would also be in the same-sex boat.[141]

Looking back at bartender guy, I caught him staring at me then glancing elsewhere in the room. Could he be gay? My gaydar senses weren't tingling. Maybe that's because I

---

[139] If you play a song that questions your feelings, you should have thought about marriage a bit more carefully.

[140] Kind of nice having the bartender keep an eye out for me.

[141] These people really know how to keep a first-time crasher entertained.

wasn't looking to have sex with anyone and was focused on staying incognito.

"Hey, I like your tuxedo," one of the sloshed guys commented.

I turned back around and smiled. "Thank you."

The brunette guy who resembled Zac Efron[142] ran his hand across the length of my arm up to my shoulder where he firmly squeezed.

I spoke too soon, the same-sex tequila boat has finally set sail for this one.

"And your beard, it's amazing!" he said stumbling over his words.

Mr. Hetroflexible was about to run his hand (or fingers) through my facial hair until Austin interrupted.

"Hey, I usually don't ask this, but would you mind giving me a hand with something in the back."

My knight in shining bowtie! Fucking thank god he came to rescue me. Don't get me wrong, Mr. Hetroflexible is cute, but he seemed like the type of guy who didn't take a *no* very well.

"Yeah, no problem," I replied. Then to Mr. Heteroflexible, I said, "Excuse me."

Placing my champagne flute on the table, I got up and followed Austin out of the reception hall, around a corner, and down a flight of stairs where the cellar was lined with bottles of whiskey, vodka, wine, and champagne.[143]

"Thanks for saving me back there from Mr. Hetroflexi-

---

[142] Just a tad.

[143] If the world is going to end, you'll know where to find me.

ble."

Austin turned and pulled me in for a deep kiss. As he was taller, I eagerly went up on my tip-toes to kiss him. His blonde scruff grazed against my beard while his soft lips tenderly introduced light bites here and there.[144]

This guy knew how to kiss!

Finally!

"I've wanted to kiss you all night," Austin admitted.

"Really? And here, I thought you were straight," I said with a smile.

"I get that a lot. Just figure it keeps people on their toes."

"Kind of like how I am right now?" I mentioned.

Deeply kissing again, he suddenly pulled back from the kiss. Was there something wrong? Austin closed the door and locked it.

What was happening?

O.M.G, I realized this would go down one of two ways; a sexual encounter, or you'd see me on the six o'clock news.

Austin turned around, loosened his tie and shirt buttons—sexy time here we come! As I tore off my tux jacket, pants, and everything else, he laid his apron on the floor, giving us something to lay on so we weren't in direct contact with the dirty floor.

What a gentleman! It reminded me of those scenes in the fifties where a guy would lay his jacket over a puddle so the woman could walk across.[145]

He laid me down gently, grazing his hand from the side

---

[144] Rubbing two beards together may start a fire.

[145] Nicholas Sparks ain't got anything on this.

of my chest down the length of my thigh. His skin was soft —too soft at that for a bartender—and there wasn't a patch of hair anywhere.[146] (I need to find out what he uses after we bang—and yes, I do think about these things during sex. I've tried to turn it off, really I tried)

"Aren't you afraid someone is going to need something from in here?" I asked.

"You ask a lot of questions, but no. I'm the only one working the wedding and I get a lunch a break—this is how I want to spend it. Plus, the sign on the bar says 'out to lunch.' So, I have thirty minutes, well, twenty-four, to be exact," he kindly explained with a smirk.

Not saying another word, I kissed him, giving him the green light to continue. The sounds of a trojan wrapper resounded in the small liquor storage room.[147]

Looking down, Austin dressed the for occasion (and he was packing, let me tell you) and after those twenty-some odd minutes passed, we found ourselves sweaty, out of breathe, and him sitting upright as I straddled him.

Austin's head laid against my chest while both of his hands gripped my hips.

"Oh man," he said, "I don't know if I can finish my shift now."

Laughing, I wiped away the sweat with my white undershirt and handed it over to my lover who did the same. He pulled me close once more and we shared another deep unblushed kiss.

---

[146] Why does this feel like I'm 007, undercover, and having one of those sexual scenes? I could get use to this.

[147] He's not playing around.

"If you're trying to initiate a second round, that's going to have wait," I flirtatiously said running my fingers through his hair.

"That sounds like an invitation and way for you to leave here with my number," he smiled.

We dressed and nonchalantly made our way back to the reception, where we came upon everyone performing the *YMCA*, including Grandma Twenty Questions and by the looks of it, the cake had been cut, which signal my departure.

"Well, it's time for me head out, kind sir," I said to Austin, sliding an empty flute glass across the bar top.

Popping another bottle of Brut, and filling my glass, he said, "that's a shame Allister. I was hopping you would stay the whole night."

Downing the glass of champagne, I smiled. Not only was the man an excellent lover, he was a charming man as well. But Austin understood I needed to leave he and wrote down his phone number on a paper napkin. Tucking it my jacket pocket, I walked behind the bar and gave him one last passionate kiss before my leaving.[148]

Walking away, I spotted the open guestbook and decided I needed to leave my mark.

Thanks for an unforgettable event—one for the books!
Allister Dean

~~14. CRASH A WEDDING~~

---

[148] God, those soft lips!

May 12, 2019

Guys!

Another ex decided to reach out! He asked to meet up for drinks. Mind you, he is in a committed relationship.

Message follows:

Ex:
Congrats on your new book!

Allister:
Haha, thanks bud.

Ex:
Bud...well 😂😂

Allister:
Does "bro" work better?

Ex:
Remember when you used to hate it when I was calling you buddy or bro 😂🩶

Allister:

Of course I do! Now that I'm much older, I don't see why it was such a big deal. I still can't believe I'm releasing a third book!

Ex:

Very, very proud of you and the titles are so you! 🖤

> **Allister:**
> Aww thanks. How's Andrew and metropolitan life?

Ex:

Listening to Rihanna now and remembering old times 😈, well, just say that we had been better.

> **Allister:**
> What do you mean?

Ex:

Everyone is watching her, but I'm watching you.

> **Allister:**
> Still don't get it. I hope everything is okay?

Ex:

Everything is okay, as a good marriage should be, right? Hey, I'm going to be in town in October or November and if you are okay, I would love to meet with you because I have unfinished business with myself that I need to close. So, hopefully you are okay with that?

Allister:
Unfinished business?

Ex:
Just my inner demons, lol jk. Don't take it seriously. I'm just wondering if you want to sit down and maybe we can just talk.

Allister:
About?

Ex:
Oh Allister, always so persuasive—I'll text you later okay. Don't worry about it and I know this is going to kill you pretty much for the rest of the night. I just want to take with you. Anyway, I have to go and I know where to find you...lol jk.

What does that even mean?

Always,

Allister

To: *Allister_at_home, August_at_home*
From: *B_at_home*
Subject: *RE: Another Ex—What Does It Even Mean!*

May 12, 2019

Dear Allister,

I think he may be lacking—in his current life—some of the things that you once fulfilled for him. This is the tough part about love. Partners only fulfill certain needs and desires. Then, we have to decide if we can live without the ones they are not fulfilling. Example: I don't know if I totally buy into the "you should marry your best friend" thing. I can have my own friends. I will fulfill that elsewhere, with my girl-friends. I don't need my man to be another girlfriend. I want to keep the lust going. I want to want to devour him. I don't ever want to enter the friend zone with my lover, but some people need their lover to be their best friend. That would be a quality they can't do without—not me.

Maybe he needs to be reminded of the qualities you have that he currently lacks in his life. Maybe he needs to see if they are everything he remembers in his mind, since we can get caught up in fantasies and distort the truth in our mind. Or, perhaps he wants to see if those qualities are what would actually fulfill him. Or, maybe he needs to be sure the grass is not actually greener.

Hmmmm....this is a toughy! I don't think a good talk over drinks could hurt anything. There is one ex that I have un-finished business with and when I was in NYC where he lives, we were not able to meet up. (He did not make it easy to do so.) It would have been nice if he had just given me that moment. I still yearn to meet up one day.

Even if only to quell the burgeoning curiosity, it may be interesting to meet up.

Do you agree?

—B

===

To: *Allister_at_home, B_at_home*
From: *August_at_home*
Subject: *RE: RE: Another Ex—What Does It Even Mean!*

May 12, 2019

Hi Allister,

Now you have to meet with that ex just to see what he has to say! Provide an escape hatch, though. Have a friend call you 20 minutes after the meeting starts.

The last time I got caught up in something a little murky like that, it was with an old friend (still current) who fooled around with me once (and fooled around with a lot of others). He wanted to tell me he had tested positive for HIV and syphilis. This was years ago, and my tests came back negative. We are still friends , that's not an easy thing to do . So that's where my head goes when I hear "we need to talk".

This sounds different. Hope your week is starting well

Talk to you later

August

To: *August_at_home, B_at_home*
From: *Allister_at_home*
Subject: *Re: Re: Re: Another Ex—What Does It Even Mean!*

May 14, 2019

After confronting my ex about his encrypted convo, he had this to say.

Message follows:

Allister:
What inner demons do you have?

Ex:

OMG lol 😂 I'm so sorry Allister! I'm now going through the conversation and I'm like god, I'm such a drunk bitch! I'm having a rough time personally but nothing crazy. Anyway, hope you are doing well and good luck with the book.[149]

---

[149] He has never talked that way before. Exposure to the gay world after all these years has really changed him—not sure if that's a good thing or not?

Allister:
Usually alcohol brings the truth out, so explain what rough times are you going through? Mind you, just from what you've told me I'm usually right about my assumptions. And we both know how much of a bad liar you are lol.

Ex:
No seriously, it was nothing crazy I swear. Just drunk and needed to talk to someone. I'm heading to work now. Nice talking to you man, we will keep in touch.

Allister:
Okay, I really don't believe you. There's something else going on you're not expressing that you're not able to communicate to Andrew, your husband. Just remember you can always talk to me about rough times and last time I checked we're friends. But like I said, your messages lead me to believe to my own conclusions.

Then my ex unfriended me on Facebook which now speaks volumes. Let's just hope that whatever is going on dissipates before any damage is done.

Always,

Allister

31

The Men of
Meerkat Manor

This is some utter bullshit!

First, there was nightmare parking on the side of a busy highway in Tahoe (and here I thought parking at Capitola Beach was terrible). Now, I'm practically tripping down an unmarked hiking path where I could potentially die if I don't watch where I'm going. All of this, of course, is to cross another item off my list and see others strip down to their birthday suits.

"How much further do we have to go?" I asked.

"Not much further," Drake assured me.

Better be.

If it weren't for the captivating scenery Tahoe offers, I

would have thrown this idea out the window, ditch Drake, and soak in the suns rays over at Sand Harbor where they have actual parking and everything is level.

Faint voices and laughter echoed throughout the wilderness and grew louder as Drake and I continued on.

"I see titties!" my straight, allied friend excitedly announced.

Had he forgotten our most important rule? "If one happens to see full-on boob first while we both are together (like actually nice boobs to gaze upon), then we may include the other party." Nobody wants to see deflated, gravity tugging knockers. But curiosity got the best of me and I looked anyway.

BAM, tits ahoy! Just as I suspected. I wasn't sure why he was all giddy about them—saggy just isn't sexy.

"Yep, flappy boobs—10 o'clock," I sarcastically responded.

Drake laughed, rolling his eyes.

"What?" I said. "I didn't think you liked geriatric breasts, or do you? If not, then don't comment."

Around the corner, up a tiny hill, and down a very steep trail, we found ourselves at *Secret Cove*. It's so secret only those of true nudist intent are present the door.[150]

It's just as beautiful as I saw in the pictures—crystal clear water, huge rocks... Ugh, no words could describe this unique mermaid lagoon.

"Before camp is setup, there's just a few rules, Allister," Drake sternly conveyed.

---

[150] Almost like Harry Potter, *The Room of Requirement*.

"Rules? At a nude beach? And here I thought there was just one rule; *Clothing may be optional.*"

"Seriously. No pictures. No lewdness.[151] And just have fun."

"I'll manage," I said, taking off my shirt.

And just like that, my friend of seven years was now nude and showing off his goods. (let's just say, I can see why the ladies keep coming back to him.)

"Whoa!" I yelled trying to censor his junk with my hand.[152]

"I'm not shy, especially if I'm here with you Allister," Drake muttered, shoving his clothes in his backpack.

"Yes, I've come to know this about you—but our friendship has always been PG-13 and it's been re-rated as R, *This friendship may contain explicit graphic scenes.*"

"It's just a penis," Drake said.

Turning my back to him and laying out my beach blanket, I said, "a penis that looks inviting! You even have guys poking up from that rock formation."

"Meerkat Manor?"

I shrugged. Was I supposed to know what that meant?

"That's the area where all the gay guys go to fuck. They pop up every so often to see who is here just so they can have sex," Drake explained with a chuckle.

"Good thing the moon doesn't exert black light otherwise we would have an eighth wonder of the world," I quipped, trying to hold back a laugh.

---

[151] I don't do that and everyone here is over the age of fifty. If anyone is being lewd, it is the sight of gravity taking over their bodies.

[152] Trying.

Drake rolled his eyes yet again.

"They should rename this place to *Ghost Baby Cove*," I added.

"All right, let's not get carried away here. Sun and good vibes here."

"Of course."

"Hey do you mind spraying my back," he said, handing over the SPF.

"Ask one of the meerkats or miss sags-a-lot over down there to do it. The only way I'm getting that close to you is if you put some shorts on," I said, not budging from my heated rock.[153]

"C'mon, I thought this was every gay guy's fantasy?" Drake said spraying his legs first and working his way up to his neck, "Please tell me you're not going to stay in your trunks the entire time?"

"Last time I checked, this is a *clothing optional* cove and I'm choosing to keep my clothes on," I conveyed adjusting my sunglasses.

My straight naked companion laughed and struggled to get sunscreen on his back.

Fuck it.

I got up and snagged the sunscreen from Drake, turned him around, and sprayed.

"Oh my god that's cold!" Drake screeched flinching forward.

"Don't be such a baby," I joked.

Handing back the SPF, I sat my happy ass back down

---

[153] The heat is a fucking doing miracles on my tense back!

on my rock and attempted to turn a shade darker.[154] Before getting comfortable, I pulled my huge blue water jug that was filled to the brim with champagne and my bluetooth speaker from my backpack.

"Any requests?" I asked Drake, setting up speaker.

"Summertime jams please," he answered.

Nodding, I opened Spotify and played the first station (out of thousands) marked *summertime* and of course the first song that played was *Cool for the Summer* by *Demi Lovato.*

I'm not going to complain—it's Demi.

Taking a swig of my bubbly, I closed my eyes and soaked up the much needed sun. It had been years since Tahoe and I were able to enjoy each others company.

Blame the copious distractions for keeping us apart, otherwise I would be near you or inside you all the time.[155]

"We've been spotted ," Drake said.

"We just arrived, of course people are going to stare. Besides, look at you. It's like you've been chiseled from marble," I said, taking another sip of my canteen wine.[156]

"You could have this body too if you stopped eating out at *Chilies*, but no, the guys are popping up from *Meerkat Manor.*"

"I've accepted the fact that I will never have six pack abs and so I decided to rock the dad bod. The corresponding diet allows me to have *Chilies*. Plus, I like food too much to

---

[154] You know that magic moment between perfect and over-done? Well, I still haven't found that moment as I always comeback looking like Sebastian from *The Little Mermaid.*

[155] Too dirty? Didn't think so.

[156] Watch, someones going to market this idea.

give it up for portion-controlled. Tupperweared rice and chicken. Starving is not attractive," I said, defending my choices.

Looking over at the rock formations, I saw not one, not two, but ten heads gawking our direction.

Creepy.

They all talked amongst themselves, and a few flexed their muscles in an attempt to enticement us.

Desperate.

"Can't they just be like normal rude people who let their unleashed dogs run rampant all over the beach, kicking up sand everywhere? I'd take that over *Meerkat Manor* any day," I told Drake.

"There's no harm, it's flattering honestly. At least we know the headcount," Drake chuckled.

"If any of come near, I'm pushing them in the lake after I belittle their manhood," I warned.[157]

• • • • •

"I'll be back," I said, getting up from my rock.

"Where are you going? Heading over to check out the guys from *Meerkat Manor*?" Drake asked.

"That's a hard no. The champagne I've been drinking is knocking on nature's door," I cutely said.

Jumping from my rock to the dirt trail, I followed it up to a nearby bush as the champagne threatened to use a bat-

---

[157] If you're going to be naked, that's one thing. If you're going to attempt to come near with said nakedness, well buddy, be prepared for some harsh comments to follow.

tering ram against my bladder.

Settling for a tree, the evacuation began.[158]

"Hi there," a voice behind me said.

Stopping midstream, I turned my head to find one of the naked meerkats smiling widely, hands on hips, checking me out.

You have got to be kidding me!

"Um, hi, do you mind? I'm kind of in the middle of something," I politely said.

"No, I don't mind. I'll wait." the naked *boyar* said.

Did I stumble upon a restroom? Was he in line? And most of all, where the hell did he come from?

"But I do and would appreciate if you just moved along so I can pee in peace," I said turning back around.

"Have it your way," he said walking past me with a smile.

Glad that was over.

Looking around to see if there were any more of those damn meerkats, I didn't see anymore uninvited guests.

Back at the rock, Drake was now on his stomach sunning his ridiculously toned ass. How is it that all these people are able to be so vulnerable and yet be so comfortable with nudity—it has to be a lifestyle choice or one who simply doesn't care.

"Everything okay back there? You were gone for a quiet a long time," Drake said in a semi-worried voice.

"I had a surprise visit from one of the meerkats who

---

[158] Yes, I just wrote a line about me peeing. Just like the book *Everybody Poops*, everybody pees.

was just standing there watching me while I did my business," I responded.

"Daring."

"Whatever," I said.

"I'll make you a bet, Allister," Drake said.

"I'm not going over there."

"Are you going to listen or cut me off again?"

"Fine, what's the bet?"I asked.

Turning back over, Drake lifted his sunglasses and made direct eye contact with me. "Go skinny dipping in the lake and I'll take you out to dinner every Saturday for the next month."

I attempted to contemplate his proposal., but failed. "I can't take you seriously when your balls are just hanging out like that."

Drake covered his manhood with his swim trunks and waited for my answer.

"Any restaurant of my choosing?" I asked.

"Yes, sir."

Fuck. I was only looking to cross off one item on my list today, not two, but I couldn't argue with free dinners for a month and it's not like I would ever see these people again. Hell, I'd never seen any of the meerkats before, let alone at any of the gay clubs.[159]

"Deal," I said, proffering my hand.

I looked around to see if the other beach participants

---

[159] My hometown is big but the gay community is small, almost like when you live in a town where everyone knows everyone.

were gazing our direction.[160]

Nothing.

Clutching my waistband, I froze. I pondered for a second and asked, "Was I about to drop trou and show off my goods for the sake of crossing off an item on my list just so I wouldn't be classified as *vanilla* anymore?"

"Any day now," Drake said laying back and tilting his head down to look past the frames of his sunglasses.

Yep.

With one swift motion, my trunks were around my ankles. Kicking my trunks away, I took a minute to enjoy my newly exposed undercarriage as it soaked in the warm rays of the sun.

"How do you feel?" Drake probed.

"Not too bad, I have to admit," I said with a smile.

"By the way, I'm impressed by the goods."

"Straight guys don't say shit like that," I told him.

"Remember, I'm heteroflexible and if you weren't one of my best friends, I'd sleep with you."[161]

Taking off my sunglasses, I glared at him with chuckle.

"Don't flatter yourself. Plus you couldn't handle this anyway."

Drake was about say something when he was stopped by roaring of cat-calls from across the beach. The men of Meerkat Manor were poking their heads out and cheering, apparently memorized by my naked body.[162]

---

[160] Correction, before dropping my shorts, I checked to see if any of the perverted guys of Meerkat Manor were watching.

[161] Heteroflexible: I'm straight, but shit happens.

[162] Or probably blinded by my severely white ass.

"Sit down before they come over and try to seduce us," Drake said.

"Let's give them a show Drake," I suggested.

Turning around to face the lake, the rocks we laid on were high enough to either jump off and cannonball or perform an elegant dive.

I chose to do an elegant cannonball instead.

Coming back up for air, I yelled a big cheer. Drake decided he was going to join and cannonballed into the water as well. Why did I wait for so long to do this? Why was I so afraid? Something about stripping naked was absolutely freeing—even exhilarating!

That is, until the Meerkat Manor guys dove into the water and swam toward us. My excitement went away after all the meerkats decided to jump in the water as well.

It was time to go before they ate us alive.

24. GO TO A NUDE BEACH

17. SKINNY DIP

To: *Eve_at_home, Lucy_at_home, Kitty_at_home*
From: *Allister_at_home*
Subject: *Katniss I Am Not*

May 19, 2019

Bitches!

In the past I've done different sports—baseball, basketball, football, BMX, tennis, swimming; pretty much everything under the athletic rainbow except for soccer. Really, really can't stand that sport.

On a whim the other day, (and after watching *The Hunger Games*), I decided take up archery and attempted to shoot arrows in my backyard. It's not as hard or complicated as it looks, (except when stringing the damn thing. There's a special tool to assist with stringing it) but one must have upper body strength in order to shoot one—let me tell you. I guess going to the gym has it perks.

Also on my mini shopping spree, a square target was also required. That fact almost slipped my mind before leaving the sporting goods store. What was I going to shoot at? Although there is a local archery range I could go to—I wasn't about

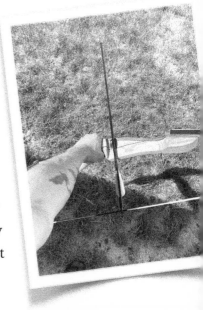

to spend even more money. I'd rather look like a damn fool in my own backyard than in front of others who've perfected this hobby.

Thought I would give you guys an update on what I was doing with the Glitter List.

I'm going to rock this bow, just in case if society ends up like the *The Hunger Games*.

Always,

Allister

P.S.,

Not a bad shot I must say.

25 ARCHERY

32

Taking Cinderella Avenue

"Are you sure about this?" Olivia asked, questioning me with overwhelming concern slapped across her face.

Could she be anymore chicken shit right now?

"Sweetie, we're in your Prius, it's 1:00 in the morning, and we're both dressed in black clothing with, hopefully, the tools we'll we need in your trunk. I think it's a bit too late to have cold feet," I said.

"What if we get caught?"

"Well... you better run fast," I sarcastically responded.

Olivia's eyes widened with fear.

"Everything will be fine. You'll be the lookout while I do the hard part."

Olivia nodded, still wide-eyed like she was about to commit murder. I would have never asked for her help if I knew she would act this way.

"By the way, why are you wearing *eyeblack grease strips*?" she asked.

"It helps reduce glare, love, " I told her, pulling the visor down and checking to see if it had smeared.

"Bitch! It's nighttime!"

"It compliments my *Mission Impossible* look, okay!" I answered.

Olivia irritatedly sighed.

Cinderella Avenue was utterly still. If you were to drop a pin, you'd hear it. Quietly getting out of the car, I popped the trunk and pulled out a pair bolt cutters, a tiny ladder, and a several Allen wrenches.[163]

I have never done anything of this nature and I've always been the type of guy who stayed on the right side of the tracks while keeping conflict at bay. In other words, I'm a wallflower.

Not tonight, Satan!

"C'mon," I said to Olivia.

We headed over to the street sign post where my reward waiting at the very top. It was probably really stupid to steal a public street sign that says Cinderella Avenue on it, but my tax dollars would do its job and the city would replace it next week if not sooner.

C'est la vie.

---

[163] Forgive me father for I don't care what I'm about to do—but I do if red and blue flashing lights appear.

"All right, I'm going to climb the ladder and cut the sign off. You need to keep an eye out and make sure no one is watching. If you see a car coming, we quickly hide until they pass," I reiterated to her for the hundredth time.

She nodded again, swallowing hard as her body trembled.

This girl was the worst side-kick ever! She would not do well in a life of crime or anything of this type of affair.[164] Setting up the ladder, I handed over the tools that I didn't need yet. Turning on a mini flash light[165] and putting it in my mouth, I climbed the ladder and began the decapitation.

"Are you done yet?" Olivia huffed.

"Just started, bitch!" I replied with a hint of force.

I'll say it again—the gym is really paying off.

• • • • •

"CAR!" Olivia screamed.

"How many times do have I have to tell you, don't scream. I'm right here."

Grabbing the ladder, we both dove behind a bush tall enough to conceal everything.

"This is a very busy neighborhood!" I told myself.

Once the street became still again, Olivia and I resumed. Forty-five minutes into the job and I barely made an inch into steel that held the sign in place. Maybe I'm go-

---

[164] Partner in crime you are not.

[165] Because the street sign was not lit; perfect for me.

ing about this wrong? There has to be a simpler way.

Getting down off the ladder, I took a second and observe a potential weakness.[166]

The only solid part of the pole was the neck, as the body was thin steel with medium size holes.

"What are you doing?" Olivia asked.

"Thinking like a criminal mastermind," I replied.

"What the hell! We don't have time for you to embody Clyde!"

"I can see why Clyde was getting fed up with Bonnie," I sharply said, wiping sweat from my forehead.

Continuing to cut through the solid piece was going to take all night—and I didn't have time for that. However, cutting through the holes would take mere seconds and I could do the rest at home in the garage.

It was settled.

Climbing up the ladder again, I started cutting the first row of holes just below the solid metal neck.

Snip, snip.

Snip, snip.

Snip, snip.

And just like that, the sign fell over—luckily onto the grass of whoever lives at the corner.

"Let's go!" I said, leaving her at the scene of the crime while jogging to the car with the ladder and cutters in one had and in the other, my sign.

"Oh. My. God! You were just going to leave me here!" Olivia loudly whispered at me.

---

[166] Yes, I do this with people too if they decide to cross me.

"Didn't you hear me say *let's go?*"

"Yea, but..."

"I'm not going to hold your hand. Now if you don't mind, I would like to leave the scene of the crime otherwise I will leave you," I sternly explained.[167]

Power walking across the street, Olivia unlocked the car and trunk—I hastily shoved everything in and climbed into the passenger side.

"Did we forget anything?" Olivia questioned looking back at where we were.

"You're impossible, you know that right?" I said glaring, "Floor it!"

"Where to?"

"My house, but don't drive like you're a part of the *Fast and Furious* crew," I said, keeping an eye out for cops.

• • • • •

In the driveway, Olivia turned off her Prius and sat there, shocked at what transpired thirty minutes ago.

"You okay?" I asked in a concerned tone.

"That. Was. Freaking. Awesome! So, exhilarating!" Olivia shouted.

"Don't go all Wynona Ryder on me now," I chuckled.

~~10. STEAL A STREET SIGN.~~[168]

---

[167] Even though it's her car.

[168] Sorry, no pictures. Can't have any evidence!

May 23, 2019

Chickees,

I wouldn't say this was the dumbest thing I've ever done in my life and yet I can now cross this off my list.

The downtown area is hosting an event (not an annual one as I believe it was somewhat last minute, and by the mayor's doing) and we decided shenanigans needed to happen. Olivia mentioned in a text there was something there with my name written all over it.

She was right.

In the heart of the event was a mechanical bull with a sign reading, *ride for five minutes and earn $20.* You best believe that your boy tried to win $20!

But he didn't.

It's a lot harder than it appears! The only thing keeping you from flying off the faux bull is a handle and a quick prayer hoping you make it out alive. I was under the impression Olivia was going to do it with me, yet, this was an excuse for her to have a good laugh at my expense from the sidelines.

I'm going to have to get her back someway!

Always,

Allister

P.S,

Sorry for the lack of pictures, it happened so fast and a line of drunk University kids who obviously thought they were capable of handling an artificial animal started to form.

This is why I always have 911 on speed dial.

20. RIDE A MECHANICAL BULL

33

Deal or No Deal,
Spice House Edition

Olivia:
Be ready in twenty minutes!

Allister:
It's 8:37pm.
I'm in bed.

Olivia:
Get up, get dressed, and be ready.

Allister:
Ugh! Fine.

"Where are you taking me?" I asked Olivia.

"It's a surprise. I figure since you made me steal a damn street sign with you, I would take you some place you haven't been before that would make you feel uncomfortable. Plus, we can cross an item off your list," she told me.

When did this bitch become so bold? From the shenanigans of *Glitter List* past, Olivia was on edge of getting caught and going to jail.

"Here, let me get you in the mood."

Olivia pulled out her phone and blasted *Pony* from its speakers.

And then it hit me.

"No, you're not," I blurted out.

Turning the corner, neon lights of every color flashed and the words *Topless, XXX,* and *Spice House* instantly caught my attention. When I wrote down stripper bar, it was under the impression it would be with guys, not busty girls who were named after kitchen ingredients.[169]

Parking the car, Olivia pulled out her wallet, "Here's twenty dollars, I figure we won't be here long."

"Is this pay back for the street sign?" I asked.

"Yep!" she replied, "C'mon, it'll be fun."

Grabbing the twenty one dollar bills, I aggressively got out of her car and hurried to the front door.

"Wait for me!" Olivia yelled.

After walking inside, damp sweat filled my nostrils, causing me to gag a little.[170]

---

[169] Cinnamon, sugar, honey—just to name a few.

[170] Why can't they mimic Disneyland and pump out good smells that create anticipation?

"If this is boob sweat I'm inhaling, we're leaving," I asserted.

"They're working girls," she replied.

Working girls or not, this wasn't what I had in mind for strippers—man sweat yes, lady sweat no. Did she not understand how pheromones work?

Sitting down at a table close to the stage, a woman wearing less than a bikini walked up to us, expertly balancing a tray of empty glasses in one hand (at tit level) and the other on her hip.

"What can I get the two of you?" she asked.

"I'll have the a cosmopolitan, and she have a water," I announced.

"A water?" Olivia asked, frowning.

"You drove me out here, you are driving me back home...sober. That makes you DD."

'That's not fair, I want to have a good time, too," she whined.

"Tough cookies."   The nearly-nude waitress disappeared with our order.

The music was a bit much and slowly building my irritation.[171] Most of the girls either looked run-down or too eager to please. What the hell was Olivia thinking, bringing me here of all places? She knows I'm pussaphobic.

"What about her?" Olivia suggested, pointing off to my left.

Nonchalantly, I looked over to see a youngish[172] work-

---

[171] One can only handle so much alternative deep pop with hard drums and bass. What is this, EDM? No offense.

[172] A couple years younger than Olivia and I.

ing girl wearing an iridescent bikini deceitfully flirting with a group of intoxicated suit and tie men.

"She looks tied up at the moment," I explained to my friend.

Out of all the girls currently present, Miss Iridescent Bikini was the freshest and seemed quite eager to fill up her g-string with singles.

"Let's keep looking around," I suggested.

The muffin-topped waitress finally served my long overdue cosmopolitan.[173]

"Come to *daddy*," I said, guiding the glass in front of me.

"Anything else I can get the two of you?" Mistress Muffin-top asked.

Olivia was about to say something when I cut her off by thanking the waitress. Then, I said turned to Olivia and said, "I told you, *no* drinks for you."

"But mama wants oneeeeeeeeee," she whined.

"Don't you ever call yourself that, especially in the place like this."

Minutes turned in hours, and more men flooded through the door. I wasn't sure if that was normal[174] or if the gents were in need of some alternative loving. Either way, I was unexpectedly enjoying myself.

"Do you mind if we sit with you two, it's just us four and there aren't enough tables in this place to go around," a guy in a well-fitting suit asked.

---

[173] Not the greatest but for tonight, it'll do. I could tell the bartender was not very generous with the vodka.

[174] If stripper bars are anything like clubs, people start pouring in around 10:30 - 11pm before the "big" drag show starts.

"Sure, take a seat," I said, waving the rest of his gang who were watching from the bar.

Olivia scooted toward me, giving the gents the other side of the table. All of them wore suits that screamed either *Macy's* or *JcPenney*. Since I found myself in need of another mediocre cosmo, I figured these gents could fulfill that.

"Let's break the ice here," I said.

Each of them look confused, as though they had never heard of that expression before.

"Or, how about we make a bet. Each of you are in suits , and I'm sure I know who the designer is. If I guess correctly, each of you have to buy me a drink, and if I don't, I have to buy each of you a drink," I wagered.

The suited gents, no longer paying any attention to the ladies of the *Spice House*, all reach over to shake my hand.

"I doubt you're going to get mine. It's custom," one of them snobbishly said with a sneer.

Who was he kidding? You would think a man of custom suits would find himself in higher class stripper bar with girls who are actually fit and not one cheeseburger away from sporting borderline muffin-top?

Please.

"Custom?" You mean altered, sweetie. Your suit is from Macy's, designer Alfani," I said in a sassy tone, "You had the jacket and the cuffs taken in."

The gang laughed, covering their mouths as though I just schooled him. Somehow, I felt like I had just channeled Julia Stiles from *Save the Last Dance*, when she told that guy she could dance circles around him.

"Olivia, be a darling and go check his jacket label," I instructed.

A nervous Olivia headed over to Mr. Custom and asked if she could look at his tag. When he nodded, she peeked at his collar. Tonight she channeled one of those *Deal or No Deal* ladies.

Looking up with the biggest grin, she announced, "Alfani!"

Brushing off my shoulder, I knew those cosmos were as good as mine.

"Blue Suit, you're also from *Macy's, The Bar* collections. Black Suit, *JcPenney, J. Ferrar,* and Mr. Grey Suit, your's is from *Kohls,* the *Apartment* collection," I said in one breathe.

Fact checking my assessments, Olivia smiled and gave a thumbs up for each of them.

Damn, I'm good.

"Okay gents, it's time to pay up," I said waving down the waitress.

"Is this your first time at a titty bar?" Mr. Blue Suit asked.

"Yes, sir. Now, where the hell is that damn waitress?" I replied tracking down the waitress.

Was it that obvious? A gay amongst the straight grain.

"How about this, since you were able to figure out our suits with such ease, you deserve a better prize than four rounds of cosmopolitan. I'm sure your friend doesn't want to take care of a drunk guy for the night," Mr. Blue Suit said with a smirk.

"I don't think she would either, but the cosmos are on the light side so I doubt any form of drunkness will happen," I said, still looking fo the waitress.

"That may be, but I feel you need a proper welcoming and a lap dance is in order. I know the perfect girl to give it to you."

Perfect girl?

Mr. Blue Suit got up and walked over to one of the working girls and slipped her a twenty.

I was nervous.

I really didn't need lap dance from any girl. Just being here was enough for me. Mr. Blue Suit came back with a huge smile on his face.

"You're in for treat."

• • • • •

When is this going to happen?

It had been forty-five minutes and the suspense was killing me. Mr. Blue Suit tipped a twenty and nothing happened.

"Olivia, honey, I'm ready to go home," I said apprehensively.

"We have to stay. You're getting a lap dance and I want to see it," she insisted.

God, why did I agree to do this? Why couldn't Olivia have been a nice friend and brought me to male strip club? The last time I checked, we both liked abs and dick.

The lights dimmed and a spotlight focused in the center of the stage. A curvy woman dragging a chair walked into the center of the light.

"I hear we have a virgin amongst us," she said softly, sensually.

Two women appeared out of nowhere behind me and gently pulled me to my feet, then guided me to the stage. Glancing back, I saw Olivia recording the whole thing with her phone.

That bitch![175]

I reluctantly did as I was told and sat on the silver steel chair she had dragged out. The spotlight completely blinded me, and the woman who called me up laid a hand on my shoulder.

"A little birdie told me that Allister has never been to a strip club before and needed to get his cherry popped," she announced.

"Oh honey, my cherry was popped by a man years ago. I don't think there's any need for a re-popping," I explained.

"Just sit back and enjoy the dance."

She wasn't going to stop or even listen to me.

"At least tell me your name?" I implored.

"LaTreasure."[176]

The opening bars of *Poor Some Sugar On Me* played on the sound system. Either she was showing her true age or this was a mandatory song a stripper must have on her playlist.

LaTreasure straddled me and pressed her breasts in my face. They smelled of sweat, whiskey, and a hint of marijuana.

Classy.

Not.

---

[175] Pictures are one thing, but video is out of the question.

[176] Her mama must have been poor or something.

She leaned, back holding onto my shoulders for support as she shimmied and whipping her long brunette hair around. Did she not realize we were now top heavy and anymore whipping of her hair might tip us over? The sea of mostly middle aged men cheered her on, unaware or uncaring of our predicament.

Fuck it. If we go down, then it's one for the books.

Letting her do her thing, it was over in a matter of three -and-a-half minutes. The blinding spotlight went off and she nonchalantly walked off the stage without looking back.

Would no one help me off the stage? All the guys went back to the individual girls they had already paid for. Is this how straight guys wanted to feel when they came here?

It was just like *Grindr,* but with live action.

Walking back to our table, Olivia giggled while the guys high-fived me.

"Thank you guys for that *lovely* dance, but now it's time for this gent to head home," I said.

"Awwwwww, I don't want to go," Olivia moaned.

"Start the Prius Olivia," I snapped.

Olivia's eyes widened and tossed back several shots the guys ordered minutes prior.

"Some advice gentleman: find yourself a real girl and not a vending machine girl. You're all handsome men. You don't want to end up like those middle-aged men over their...single, sad, and desperate for attention," I said.

And just like that, I left the Spice House.

12. ~~STRIPPER BAR~~

To: *August_at_home*
From: *Allister_at_home*
Subject: *You'll Shoot Your Eye Out Kid*

June 3, 2019

Dear August,

I can happily report that I officially went out in the middle of nowhere and fired a gun. Don't know what type of gun it was, except that it was a hand gun. Just like cars, I know nothing about them except for how to operate them.

The kick from the gun is a lot harsher than expected. Almost shot my eye out, honestly. Someone suggested I purchase one and my response was simple but yet perfect: only if they can make it pink with a diamond handle.

That's the only way I'll ever buy a gun.

Always,

Allister

~~8. SHOOT A GUN~~

To: *August_at_home*
From: *Allister_at_home*
Subject: *Happy Pride!*

June 15, 2019

Dear August,

To get into the spirit of queer things, I decided it was the perfect month to do something I would have never done in my twenties. And after a religious viewing of the movie *Sex and the City*, my gut told me it was time to expand on my gay-hood and purchase my first pair of heels. I found a decently priced knock-off version of the blue pair Carrie wore for her wedding.

Most of the gays of older generations (non drag) have already walked in stilettos, making this undocumented right of passage I never knew about.

Waiting for about week, I ripped the box open and prayed they fit as I slipped them on, totally embodying Cindefella—they fit perfect! Thank god, I had been going through too many returns on Amazon.

After walking around the house and falling a dozen times, I hold a newfound respect for those who enjoy a good heel—both women *and* men.

Always,

Allister

~~9. WEAR & WALK IN HEELS~~

34

Tacos and the City

"Girl, we're here!" I proudly said to Alex with a huge grin on my face.

Alex roared with excitement and waved her hands in the air. After crossing the Golden Gate Bridge, the sudden feeling of home rushed through my body. Though I was just in San Fran for Folsom Street Fair, it had been five years since my last attendance of Pride.[177]

My Prides of times past were a complete shit-show and I blame my so-called *friends*, who come to find out were only trash-talking me behind my back.

---

[177] We had also stopped to fuel up before hand and stumbled upon a field of sunflowers as far as the eye could see! Kodak moment.

This time around, I had nothing but good company—Alex (from the podcast), Kitty, and her boyfriend.

Something told me (now that I'm thirty) that this time around would be one to remember.

I felt it in my gut.

Parking the car in the hotel garage, and with Alex on a mini smoke break, I checked us in. Making it a tradition, I decided to book at *The Carriage Inn*,[178] a hotel with an abundance of rooms named after local or well-known celebrities.[179]

"Are you ready to head up, love?" I asked Alex.

"Hell ya!" she said, tossing her cigarette to the ground and stepping on it.

Grabbing our bags and rollable luggage, we headed upstairs and it brought back fond memories. Well, the good ones that didn't contain unnecessary drama from the guys of my plastic days.

"Room 310, Ambrose Bierce. Never heard of him," I said to Alex, inserting the key card into the door.

Once inside, we took a look around and then threw our heavy baggage on the floor and laid on one of the two queen beds together, taking a celebratory inhale of *we made*

---

[178] If you ever decide to hit up good old San Fran, book with The Carriage Inn. You'll be in for a treat.

[179] We won't get into details about the room I was in when I first booked with them.

it in one piece.

"We need to get ready dear, we have the *Passing of the Leather Vests* to attend!" I told my Pride companion.

Alex nodded, willed herself up from her bed, and walked into the bathroom to touch up her makeup—which would take a hot second.

Just like as Prides before, the corner of the room hosted an oblong table with a very old typewriter. A piece of paper with a passage about the famous person in which the room was named after was threaded in it.

Curiosity killed me.

Ambrose was a short story writer, journalist, and civil war veteran and a sibling of seven who all had names that started with the letter A. The writer disappeared, becoming one of the most famous in American History.

"Hey, we're staying in a missing writer's room!" I yelled to Alex.

"How do you know that?" she asked.

"Says on the piece of paper. Everyone room has one about who the room is named after."

"Charming!" Alex commented, "What time does this thing start?"

"It starts at 7:00. You and I will head there, make an appearance, and go from there. Not sure when Kitty and her boyfriend will arrive—they're coming from San Jose after Kitty gets off from her job," I explained.

"I'm ready when you are, then," Alex said grabbing her clutch.

We hit the streets of San Francisco (again) and already, we found ourselves heading the wrong direction.

Damn it.

"First, let's take our first official Pride Weekend picture," I suggested, standing in front of pole sporting the rainbow flag.

Alex quickly fixed her hair, and I counted to three—but was interrupted at two when a dirty homeless woman placed her arms over our shoulders, thinking she was going to be included in the picture. Both of us instantly pulled out from under her and walked away. No matter how many times I come back, I alway forget how bad the homelessness problem is.

"I can't believe that just happened!" I disgustingly said.

"I know," Alex responded.

"Does anyone have hand sanitizer or a moist alcohol toilette?" I said loudly.

"She wasn't that dirty, Allister."

"Um...sweetie, we weren't exactly touched by an angel," I sassed back.

Several blocks later, I checked the map on my phone to find the bar the event was at.

"What's this place called again?" Alex asked.

"*Powerhouse*," I said, "Never heard of this place before. According to the map, it's not too far."

"Good, because I am sweating up a storm here," Alex said fanning her face with her hand.[180]

After a few blocks and a few wrong turns, my home girl and I made it to our destination. The outside was severely dated, sporting a 90s look at best: solid grey with blue and

---

[180] I looked away for a second and it was like she just ran a marathon.

black stripes on the door and the name just above the door frame.

"I need the bathroom!" Alex yelled.

Inside, the atmosphere was very much like a bar I know back home (Fivestar)—barely any lighting, a very small dance floor with a high-rise stage, and an area in the back. The only thing that was different were the multiple televisions scattered through out the bar that played hardcore gay porn.

"O.M.G.!" I screamed.

Embarrassed, I covered Alex's hetero virgin eyes as though she was one of my kids watching a movie when out of the blue, a sex scene pops up.[181]

"Stop, it's not like I haven't seen gay porn before," she said, walking her sassy self over to the bartender to ask where the restroom was.

Watching her walk up some stairs to the next level, I knew it was time for our first Pride drink.

But what to order?

Usually, she and I order wine or champagne, but never anything hard. We're in the city, it's Pride, and we're in a bar where they're playing hardcore[182] (oh god, I looked up at the screen again) porn...

"Hi. Mr. Bartender," I said, waving him down.

He causally walked over, wiping his hands with a dish towel. He smiled and waited for me to place my order.

"Can I please have two cosmopolitans, extra strong?"

---

[181] We've had one of those moments with our parents one way or another.

[182] More like stomach turning.

Investile
Bare Chest Calendar Photo by Dot
June 28, 2019

Nodding, he pulled two martini glasses from a neon shelf behind him and concocted the perfect opening drinking number.

• • • • •

Checking my phone, there was still no text or missed called from Kitty to me know they were on their way or at the hotel.

"Honey! Put your phone away, they'll reach out. Don't worry," Alex said, handling another round of cosmos.

"You're right, I just don't want to get into party mode and miss their call and find they are stranded at the front desk wondering what the hell is goin gon," I said, sipping my refilled pink drink.

Placing my phone in my back pocket, a familiar face walked through the front door and I instantly waved him down.

"Hey! You made it!" Jordan said, greeting us.

"Wouldn't miss it for the world! Jordan this is Alex, an amazing girl who you don't want to ever forget. She also is the creator of the podcast *The Hate Journals*," I said giving my homegirl a meaty introduction.

"Does he do your advertising?" Jordan said, gently nudging Alex

After some small talk, Jordan took me around the bar and made small introductions with the other men of the Leather calendar who would be receiving their vest—this also included guys from past calendars as well. Everyone was exceptionally nice, but I could feel their eyes sizing me up—almost like each of the guys could smell my Nevada stench.

Fresh meat.

As the bar filled up and the time approached 7:00, my phone alerted me of a text from Kitty.

"We're pulling into the hotel!"

"Shit!" I said loudly.

I quickly downed my third pink drink and told Alex, that Kitty and her boyfriend were at the hotel.

"Go, go! I'll be right here and don't you worry about me. I can handle myself," Alex confidently said, scooting me toward the door.

Running, there was only fifteen minutes of sunlight left before certain landmarks disappeared (something I learned from my mother whenever traveling. It keeps you from getting lost in a big city).

Up a few blocks, and turning the corner, I was back at the hotel where the couple waited for me in the lobby.

"Sorry it took me so long," I panted.

"What are you talking about? It was only ten minute wait. You didn't have to run," Kitty said coming in for a hug.

"Every minute counts this weekend," I said with a smile.

Giving Taron a hug, I grabbed a bag or two and guided them up to the Ambrose room—using the elevator ride up to explain who he was.

• • • • •

"On our way, love," I texted Alex.

The three of us stopped at Subway to grab a bite to eat before our night of possible binge drinking. Kitty was already regretting the sandwich idea as hers was already pulling apart and soggy.[183]

DING!

Must be from Alex.

"Meet us at *The Eagle*."

The Eagle? Had we missed what was left of the vest ceremony? I thought we had enough time to make it back and catch the end of it, but it was over.

Sigh.

"Change of plans guys. Everyone is migrating from *Powerhouse*[184] to *The Eagle*," I explained to Kitty and Taron.

"I hope Taron and I didn't cause you to miss anything from the event you were at?" Kitty apologized.

"Sweetie, it's okay. The bar I just came from wasn't exactly your kind of scene," I said.

Kitty raised an eyebrow. I wasn't about to subject her to live-action gay porn. Her semi-virgin eyes couldn't handle that amount of anal penetration.

No, we're going to *The Eagle*.

---

[183] Forever a *Port of Subs* guy.

[184] Thank god.

• • • • •

"Where the fuck is Alex?" I said, beginning to worry.

She should have been the first one here. From our last conversation, Alex made it sound as though she was en route. I called her again, but she didn't pick up.

What the hell?

"Guys, I'm starting to get worried," I expressed to Kitty and Taron.

"She'll be here. Don't worry. We're in San Francisco and like you said, Alex is with a bunch of gay men who *promised* they would take care of her," Kitty said.

As much as I wanted to calm down and hope for the best, I couldn't. If I indeed lost her, what would I tell her husband? "I lost your wife in San Francisco, my bad."

Yeah, right!

Calling her phone again, a familiar voice on the other end answered, "hello."

"Alex! Where the hell are you? Are you okay?" I screamed into the phone while plugging my other ear with my finger to hear better.

"Yes, yes, yes. The guys and I are almost to *The Eagle*," she explained.

"What's taking so long?"

"I was hungry. So, I stopped at one of the street vendors for tacos," Alex chuckled.

What? This chick, who had me on the edge of a heart attack, ready to hit the streets shouting her name, decided to make a pitstop because she was hungry for tacos?

Alex so owes me a drink when she gets here!

I took a yoga inhale and calmed down, "Okay. I was just a little worried. Take your time getting here and enjoy your tacos."

Ending the phone call, I looked over at Kitty and Taron, who gave an, "is everything okay," stare, and I reciprocated with a small smile and a thumbs up.

Heading to the bar, the cute bartender (while wiping his hands with a white wash cloth) asked for my order.

"Can I get two shots of Fireball and an extra strong Cosmopolitan that would have Carrie Bradshaw fall on her ass?"

June 30, 2019

Dear August,

I have a moment to write to you while the gang I'm with procure provisions for the day.

This morning Alex told us that either we had a ghost or a mouse and wanted to check us out from the hotel. Last night she awoke to the sounds of a crinkling wrapper—"it was like crinkle, crinkle...crinkle, crinkle," as she put it. At first, she thought it was a haunting in progress and then remembered we stopped for the snacks before we got to San Fran. Her mind instantly jumped to a mouse.

But come to find out, it was just drunk Kitty trying not to wake anyone in the middle of night while attempting to pull the plastic wrapping off a plastic cup to get water.

"Girl, just rip the plastic shit off!" she told Kitty this morning.

Why is it that I alway miss the best shit? Oh, and apparently, I have sleep apnea as Alex had to kick me back to life in bed when I stopped breathing. She suggested that I get checked out—that's a huge maybe on my part.

Anyways, gotta go. Everyone is ready to make their purchases.

Always,

Allister

35

A Midsummer's Day Pride

— PRIDE WEEKEND: DAY TWO —

We decided a day of soaking in the sun and listening to a wide range of live music at *Delores Park* was needed after last night's shenanigans between *Powerhouse* and *The Eagle*.

On our way, we stopped at Safeway to grab a few essentials—yogurt parfaits, chips, and lots of champagne. It was the right combination for the first night's recovery.[185]

Out of all the San Francisco Prides I attended, never, not once, had I attended any of the events happening at *Delores*.[186]

---

[185] We went a little too hard.

[186] We won't mention any names.

Even Eve made a special hour trip down from San Jose (though it was her boyfriend's birthday weekend) to come chill with us—it wouldn't be Pride without her.

"Allister!" a voice said from behind me.

Turning around, a good friend (Becky) who I hadn't seen in months since she moved back to California came barreling up to me with open arms.

"OMG! I didn't know you were going to be here!" I yelled, embracing her.

"It was last minute, honestly. Anyway, this is my girlfriend, Cassandra."

Behind Becky stood a smiling girl , seemingly unsure if she should give me hug or shake my hand.

"Hi there! I've heard so much about you, and don't worry it's all been good things," I said, aggressively hugging her.[187]

"I have to say the same," she said.

"This is Eve, Kat, Taron—her boyfriend, and Alex. She started the podcast *The Hate Journals*," I said.

"Nice to meet you all."

"Now that we've gotten that out of the way,

---

[187] The champagne buzz was kicking in.

who wants gummy bears soaked in vodka?" Becky asked.

One by one, each of us passed the ziplock bag around, ingesting a decent amount of gummy bears. Every time something like this comes my way, it's usually made way too strong and it burns my throat on the way down.

Ugh.

Downing the rest of my champagne, I couldn't help but notice two shirtless guys wearing matching knee high rainbow socks and unicorn shorts walking past my camp over to the group of girls several feet away.[188]

Why did they look so familiar?

And then it hit me like a ton of bricks, it was Sean Cody pornstars Brayden and Josh. The only other time I had been this close to a Sean Cody pornstar (Brysen) was at *FACESNV*.

I watched Brayden and Josh greet the bundle of girls and wondered if I should ask them if they wouldn't mind posing for a picture. I didn't want to impede on their good time, or out the guys if the girls didn't know about their *acting career*.

"Why are you watching those guys so intently?" Kitty asked.

"Well, my dear, you're in the presence of professional gay pornstars," I said, not breaking eye contact.

"What where?"

"My three o'clock. The ones in the knee-high white rainbow socks."

"Gay porn stars!" Becky yelled.

"Jesus, I don't think China heard you," I said turning my

---

[188] They even had matching shoes.

back to the couple.

"And why are we even talking about them?" Kitty asked.

"I think it'd be fun to get a picture with them."

"Get over there then," Becky pushed.

Grabbing my phone, I opened my camera app and started to walk over but found myself immediately stopping—Brayden and Josh were gayer than me![189]

Both had a limp wrist, a jetted hip, walked with an extra skip in their step, and on top of that, really didn't have great bodies. Of course, you could tell they worked out, but Josh had the beginnings of a beer belly.

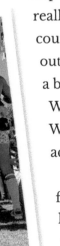

What happened to his abs?

What happened to their straight-acting personas?

It's not like I'm their biggest fan[190] or anything, but it's such a let down to find out how phony a people can be once in front of a camera. It's like finding out Santa or the tooth fairy isn't real all over again.

"Thought you were going to get a picture with them?" Becky said.

"I don't want to interrupt them. If our paths cross again, I'll get a picture then," I explained. "Now, where are those

---

[189] People say that when I walk into a room, they can tell right then and there.

[190] My biggest fan is Tanner, but he's no longer making videos with Sean Cody. But the silver lining of it all is that I follow him on Instagram.

gummy bears?"

"Here, take them. They are really strong. Plus, I need to used the bathroom," Kitty said, getting up. She made her way through the crowed toward the port-a-potties with alarmingly massive lines.[191]

"Shouldn't someone go with her?" I said.

"I think she's okay," Eve replied.

Shrugging my shoulders, I carried on eating more vodka gummy bears—it's Pride, it doesn't hurt to get just a tad bit tipsy.

An hour and forty-five minutes later...

"Shouldn't have Kitty been back by now?" Alex asked, concerned.

Alex and I had returned from the bathroom ourselves but when I didn't see Kitty with Eve, Taron, or Becky, Alex's question activated my inner *papa bear.*

"Taron, has Kitty called you at all?" asked.

"No, I haven't gotten any calls or texts."

"You wouldn't. Any sort of signal, data or voice, is convoluted with this amount of people in one location. Eve I want you to try and call her and see where she is?" I said, now acting group leader.

"Wait! She's calling me," Taron said.

We remained quiet, waiting for confirmation that she was okay.

"Okay, I'll be right there."

---

[191] Gay Pride bathroom lines are way worse than standing in line for rides at Disneyland.

"Is she okay? Has she been kidnapped or arrested?" I asked.

"No, she fainted while waiting in line for the bathroom," he replied.

Taron and Eve sprinted off to the paramedic area, where they were keeping Kitty. Maybe it was heat exhaustion that made her faint? I hadn't seen her drink any water all day. Regardless, the case of the missing Kitty was now solved—which meant I could continue drinking a lot more champagne.

• • • • •

Once Taron and Eve retrieved Kitty and returned thirty minutes later, she explained what happened to her.

"One second everything was fine and the next, I woke up on the ground," Kitty said.

"And this is why we use the buddy system," I said with a chuckle.

"Don't worry though, when I came to, I was surrounded by all theses pretty lesbians who were stroking my hair and telling they weren't going to leave my side," Kitty said with a laugh.

"Wow, sounds like the beginnings of a porno," Eve chipped in.

"That or a lesbian's wet dream. Either way I felt so much love from each of them. This is what Pride is all about!" Kat said.

Passing out, creating severe panic, and teasing a large group lesbians.

Yes, this is what Pride is all about.

36

Duck, Duck, Clark

"Did you guys want Dim Sum for lunch?" Kitty asked.

"I've never had Jim Sum," I responded.

Kitty couldn't help but laugh, "Honey, it's called Dim Sum with a D."

"Whatever it's called, I volunteer as tribute."

Alex was already out the door, luggage in hand, and a cigarette dangling from her lips, ready to light.

After ditching our cars in a nearby parking garage, we were now in the heart of China Town.

Inside and already seated, I noticed the restaurant walls were lined with Chinese tapestry, bold black pillars, and jade sculptures in the shape of dragons. Though everything had a place, I was the only person out of the place.

All eyes were on me.

There I was wearing booty jean shorts that were rolled up at the bottom, a blue bro-tank, white Toms, and gold and blue glitter around my eyes—including in my hair.[192]

"I should have gotten ready in a bathroom after this," I said to everyone.

"You look great!" Alex said with encouragement.

"Yes, that is correct. But, my nipples are peeking out from the sides of my tank, screaming 'hello,' and I feel such severe judgement coming from everyone who's not seated at our table."

Alex, Kitty, and Taron scoped the room, making eye contact with practically everyone who also craved Dim Sum.

"Guys, stop looking around," I told them.

Quickly getting over my insecure feeling, I asked Kitty how Dim Sum worked.

"It's simple. They hand you a card and you fill it out. Then, the ladies with carts check the card and give you want you ordered if their card has it. Each cart has something different in it."

"Sounds like fun!"

And just like that, women with carts made their way down the narrow aisles, filling out customer cards and handing out plates of hot dumplings.

"Have you ever had duck before?" Taron asked.

"Never!" I said.

"Get ready, because you're about too," Taron said.

---

[192] The kind of glitter cheerleaders sport when at a high school football game.

I'm probably one of the last millennial adults who hasn't tried duck. Looking back on all the times I've shoved my hand out in front of a new food before instantly rejecting the idea of trying it, one has to ask why?

The saying, "Don't knock it till you try it" is something I wished I advocated for in my adolescent years. My food horizon would be much less cumbersome.

Taron ordered four duck dumplings and handed over the card for the carters to fill out, and soon a duck dumpling rested on a plate before me.

Steam rose, allowing me to smell the delicious aroma it gave off. Grabbing my chopsticks, I took a gigantic bite, letting every flavor overwhelm my tastebuds. The duck inside was smothered in some sort of barbecue sauce, giving the dish an extra kick.

Closing my eyes, I moaned with delight. I was in Chinese heaven.

"Seems Allister likes it," Kitty said with a smile.

"I'm having a relationship with my duck dumpling at the moment," I responded, my eyes still closed, "I may cream my pants."[193]

Alex laughed loudly, and a few nearby patrons turned around in wonder.

Bring on the fucking duck!

• • • • •

After many carts of Dim Sum, Taron graciously paid for lunch. Then we headed down to the Civic Center, where millions of people gathered to celebrate the last day of Pride.

Live music (stages on every corner), vendors of all sorts,

a leather alley[194] hidden behind a blue tarp, an endless supply of condoms and lube being passed out, and without a doubt long, long, long lines for the use of the port-a-pottys—always a crowd favorite.

Rather than fight through the crowd, we sat our asses down on the grass a few yards from the main stage. The music artist line-up for this year wasn't exactly worth getting excited

---

[193] Duck, oddly enough, tastes just like chicken—but greasier, for sure.
[194] Where you can get whipped.

over. Three Prides ago, they had Steve Grand, Todrick Hall, and Betty Who.

Oh well, I guess.

I was much more interested in the group of people on top of a tall, box-like structure. At any minute, it seemed like someone would plummet to the ground, and certain doom.

Even though there was grass beneath the box-thing, one could still break a femur.

"Who wants a beer?" Alex suggested.

"I'll grab us the first round," I offered.[195]

"Do you want me to come with you?" Taron asked.

"I got this."

Up on my feet, I marched over to the beer vendor tent and took my place in a very long line. Let me take back what I said about the lines at the port-a-pooty's: this line was much worse.

People watching and eavesdropping, I couldn't help but enjoy my environment—even though I was a thirty-year-old guy surrounded by baby gays who thought they had a solid grasp on life.

A bit of sadness came over me—I didn't want to go home, which meant I had to go back to reality. San Francisco, though they have a severe bum problem, was my city. The best way to put is this...San Francisco is to Allister Dean as New York is to Carrie Bradshaw.

I feel most at home when I'm here.

I was on the verge of just saying "fuck it," starting some-

---

[195] Nothing like a good old fashion Bud to end the weekend.

thing new, and not returning to my hometown. That's how much I'm in love with this city.

Making it to the front of line, I handed over my driver's license to show that I was old enough to drink for two fifteen-year-olds. "Four Bud Lights please." After the bartender swiped my credit card and handed it back, I looked past the beer vendor cart and my stomach tightened into knots.

On the other side, waiting for his beer order, stood Clark. Sporting platinum hair and a romper, he and I made unbreakable eye-contact. I hadn't seen or spoken to him since February. By now, he probably discovered that I used him for an article to build my portfolio.[196]

My body froze.

What were the odds he and I would come (somewhat) face to face in a convoluted area months down the road. I suspected that after things ended between us, that would the last time I'd see him— but, life had other plans.

Was he going to come over here?

Did he want to talk?

Did he want to kick my ass?

Though I would understand, what I did next seemed appropriate.

Giving him a smile, I tilted my head to him before grabbing

---

[196] Worst mistake I've ever made.

the beer. Walking off, I turned around for one gaze upon Clark, "Please let this be the last time I run into him," I said to myself.

And just like that, he smiled, reciprocating the same head tilt.

It was the perfect place/time to leave Clark.

Back on the greener side of the pastures, I handed out the beers, asking what I had missed.

"Someone fell off the square block behind you," Kitty said, taking a sip of her beer.

"I fucking knew that would happen!" I said, sitting back down on the grass.

"You were gone for a hot second, everything ok?" Taron mentioned.

"Nothing I couldn't handle. Now, who wants to bet another dumb kid falls off the square block again?" I asked.

"I'll take that bet," Kitty said with a smile.

~~7. TRY A DIFFERENT FOOD~~

37

The Curious Case
of Rex Tuggington

Knock, knock.

I stood outside apartment sixty-six, cold as hell, holding a bottle of *Black Ink* red blend wine while listening attentively for any signs of life from inside.

The door opened quickly and behind it was a thirty-something blonde gentleman who greeted me with a smile.

"Hi there."

Making a quick assessment, I felt surprised. I wasn't expecting him to be as tall as me. In the photos he shared, he appeared to be on the shorter side.

Regardless, Rex was cute.

"Sorry, I'm a bit early. Didn't expect to be so quick at

the store when I bought the wine," I apologized.

"No, no, you're fine. C'mon in, I'm just finishing up with some soup I'm meal prepping my weekday lunches," he said, placing a hand around my shoulder and pulling me through the door.

Rex took the wine, and I took off my coat and hung it over one of the table chairs while slowly taking in how bland his apartment was. Nothing matched. All the pieces he collected were old and bought from an antique store.[197]

"How long have you lived here?" I asked.

"A little over a year or so," Rex answered, stirring his homemade soup.

Covering his soup, he reached in his cupboard and pulled out two different wineglasses.

"Sorry they don't match."

"No worries," I said, lying to his face.

Someone who works at the university as a music professor and has lived in an apartment for a year or so should have invested in a set of wine glasses.

"...and I should purchase a set of knives, too," Rex added.

The eclectic decorum, the mix-matched dish-ware; it's like he never left the fraternity or college life. On top of that, he was a newly-minted bisexual man to society.

I had to ask, even if it was rude and ignorant, "How does bisexual work?"

Rex chuckled. He poured his soup into a large container and rinsed out the pot used.

---

[197] Digging the vintage wooden skies, though.

"What do you mean?"

"Well, do you one minute like men and then suddenly have the urge to change to women? When did you first realize you were bisexual?"

He took a deep breathe and poured wine into the mismatched glasses and dove into his story, "I fell in love with a male coworker. He and I worked very closely, and our professional relationship evolved to the point of mutual attraction. But it couldn't continue because he was married. I never meant for it to happen."

Cliché.

"And I don't switch on and off when it comes to men and women. It's all about attraction," Rex said.

That mades sense.

"Like right now, I have a handsome guy I would really like to be close to."

And just like that, Rex led me to the couch, placed my wine glass on the coffee table, and planted his lips upon mine. His kiss was very smooth, light, and yet aggressive.

This went on for hours.

Clothes were shed.

We found ourselves naked, cuddling on a blanket in front of a roaring fire.

Like I said, cliché.

Getting up, I walked over to the kitchen and poured the last of the wine I had brought. I sat back down and stared into his eyes. For a brief moment, I felt like one of those Harlequin romance novels—until...

"There's something I want to tell you," Rex said, running his hand over my thigh.

Perplexed, I knew this was too good to be true. No one ever gets to have a romantic night by the fire and get away with it—there's always a catch soon to follow.

"Yes," I replied.

"Something was taken from me."

I couldn't help but laugh and when I looked at him, Rex's had a concerned look about him.

"Oh, you're serious," I said, taking a swig of wine.

Taking the glass from my hand, he placed it on a nearby end table and continued. "My foreskin was taken from me. Don't you think parents should allow their kid to make the choice of keeping it or not? That's why I'm trying to regrow it."

What the hell? Did he not understand that once it's gone, it's gone? It's not like hair or nails. That's fucking wild![198] A follow-up question was in order.

"And how does one grow it back?"

"I've been doing research online. Other than plastic surgery, there have been cases of guy just tugging on their dicks. Since I've been doing that, slowly but surely, I've made progress," Rex proudly said.

I repeat, that's fucking wild!

Rex got up and gave me a brief tutorial on how his tugging process worked and how *effective* it was (which it wasn't). Why do the cute guys tend to be the crazy guys? I wondered if the coworker he fell in love with fucked him up?

Just before I can finish another thought...

---

[198] Alex, you're rubbing off on me.

"Oh shit," Rex said.

That's never a good sign. Did he yank too hard and rip some dick skin? I could see it playing out in my mind: "How did this happen?" a nurse asks. "Well, he was showing me his tugging technique for regrowing his foreskin," I answer.

"What? I asked, looking up at Rex.

"I just came."

Looking down at his dick, I saw his hand was covered in semen.

It had become officially weird.

Getting up, I swiftly got dressed, telling him it was a rather interesting evening but, darn it all, I had something I forgot that needed to be done.

Rushing out the door, I drove home utterly flabbergasted at what just ensued. Within minutes, a text from Rex came through: "Hope I didn't scare you off."

Scared doesn't quite cover it.

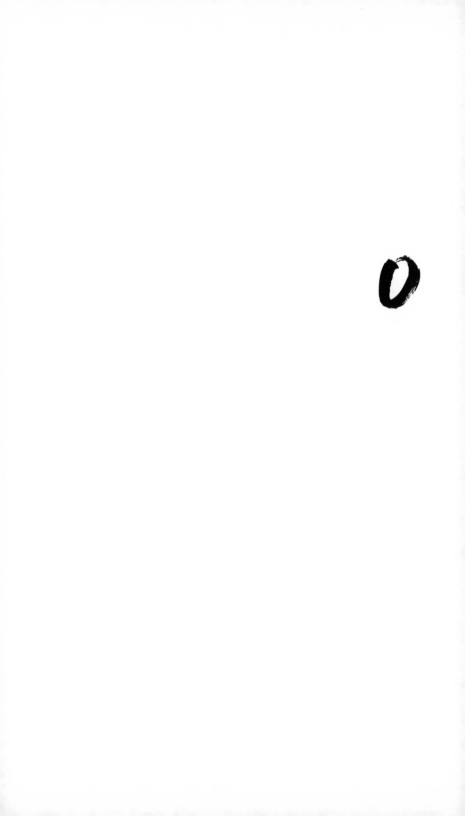

Extravagant Gays on Social Media,

After spending a complete year doing so-called extravagant activities, I have to say...aren't you fucking tired? I sure as hell am. Day in, day out of endless planning to keep my life from feeling dim is nerve-wracking.

What pills are your doctors prescribing to keep you motivated, and yet, coming undone at the seams?

Nonetheless, you can keep it all. I'm pretty content staying at home, eating a tub of raw cookie dough in a peel-off face mask, subdued by Netflix, and enjoying the confines of my own bed, much less than being in others.

Allister

To: *August_ at_ home*
From: *Allister_ at_ home*
Subject: *What A Year!*

July 2, 2019

Dear August,

Here I am—another year older, another year wiser, another year bolder. Is it wrong of me to have had severe doubt in myself?

This will be my final letter to you. I personally wanted to thank you for virtually standing by me through this chaotic year.

OH! Before I forget, I took a train with some friends to the next town over, buzzing on bubbly from a thermos. By the time we got there (it was only a two hour ride) everyone was ready to enjoy the day ahead.

So, there you have it—thirty items in year.

Always,

Allister

30. ~~TAKE A TRAIN~~

38

Never Have
I Ever: Part II

"Hi, yes, your house merlot, please?" I asked the bartender, seating myself in one of the high-chairs.

My favorite bar, The Emerson, was unexpectedly packed for a Saturday evening—usually, 9:00 p.m. is the kick off time for nocturnal activities around these parts.[199]

The bartender presented a nearly half-filled wine glass in front of me, and when I sipped it, my taste buds immediately awoke. It had been a long time since I went out by myself and enjoyed an enigmatic night.

Taking another large sip of the full-embodied juice that quenched my thirst, everything else around me faded and

---

[199] Pregaming at 7:00 pm is also the social norm.

nirvana hit.

"That's one of my favorites."

Parting my lips from the glass, "And why is that?"

A woman, barely hitting thirty-five, smiled widely with a chuckle and turned her entire body in my direction.

"Because it's made here locally by a bunch of broads who have nothing better to do other than create perfection," she explained. "I'm Ann, one of the bartender leads here."

I knew she looked oddly familiar. I've been in The Emerson a handful of times, and every time she was the bartender who helped me.

"I'm Allister. I knew I was having déjà vu with you," I said.

"So, what brings you here by yourself?"

"Well, if you must know Miss Ann, I recently completed my Glitter List a few days ago and I needed a fabulous glass of wine to celebrate my victory," I shared.

"Glitter List?" Ann quizzically asked.

"An extravagant mission to accomplish absolute fierceness or something like that. But really, in June of last year I composed a list of thirty items to complete in a year—last month was the end of that year."

"Fascinating! What made you decide to create such a list?"

"Besides noticing how vanilla my life was during my twenties, it was a couple rounds of *Never Have I Ever*," I said with a chuckle.

"I haven't played that game since high school. No time like the present, I always say," Ann said raising her hand up with five fingers.

"You have to be kidding me?"

Seriously?

Was this effervescent bartender initiating the drinking game that created such a chaotic year for me?

Admittedly, my chaotic year was actually really fun—extremely exhausting, but fun nonetheless. My horizons widened, allowing me to comfortably say yes without fear or regret, and that's something I'll always cherish till the day I die—I've crashed a stranger's wedding, for fuck's sake.[200]

Maybe I'll get that engraved on my headstone; Here lies Allister Dean, wedding crasher.

Has a nice ring to it.

"What the hell!" I said, raising my hand.

Hopefully now, some of my fingers go down.[201]

---

[200] I hope both newlyweds enjoy the mind-fuck of trying to figure who I am once they view the wedding photos.

[201] If they don't, we've got a serious problem.

Acknowledgements

I feel so lucky to have a rambunctious group of misfits who are willing to venture into the "unknown" and create some rockin' memories.

This memoir would have never been possible without any of you!

My San Jose bunch, never change who are.

The Hate Journals, I am so glad we met. May that be over a glass of wine or champagne because it's never a dull moment.

Alex, what can say except…god, I love you! There, I said it.

August, my pen pal, you are my man behind the curtain from the land of Oz guiding me, in a way, to make much more logical decisions.

And last, but not least, my editor Damien. There is not enough gratitude in the world to give you for taking the time out of your day (even with a new baby) to make these pages bleed (digitally, of course), making sure I don't sound utterly stupid by fixing my grammar and spelling errors. And I apologize for making you edit my acknowledgment to you.

Thank you is not enough to express how I feel.

About the Author

Allister Dean is the author of two memoirs *Deliciously Wicked* and *Brutally Bitter*. He lives in Nevada with his two mischievous chihuahuas, Mercury and Mars. Allister is no longer single and venturing into the world of love again.

God, help us all—just kidding.

Visit allisterdean.com to learn more.

Lightning Source UK Ltd.
Milton Keynes UK
UKHW010603100320
360054UK00002B/55/J